DIVERS

DIVERS

Jon May

Hodder & Stoughton

British Cataloguing in Publication Data
May, Jon
Divers
I. Title
627.72

ISBN 0-340-63529-0

Typeset by Hewer Text Composition Services, Edinburgh
Printed and bound in Great Britain by
Mackays of Chatham PLC, Chatham, Kent

Hodder and Stoughton
A division of Hodder Headline PLC
338 Euston Road
London NW1 3BH

This is the story of the deep-sea diving industry, and the incidents, and the people that take part in them, all existed. Where using a real name might have either given offence or perhaps stirred the memories of those left too cruelly, I have altered a name, a date, or a place.

There are far too many people who have helped me in the construction of this work to name them all but I remember them, all of them, in most cases with affection.

Too many men have lost their lives in the history of the offshore oil business for any single dedication to be appropriate, but to those lost pioneers this book is dedicated, and to their families who will never, ever, forget the real price of oil.

J.M.

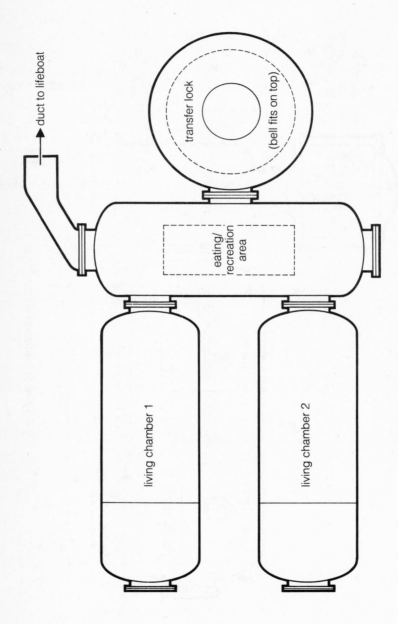

Dive chamber layout (based on the *Seaforth Clansman*)

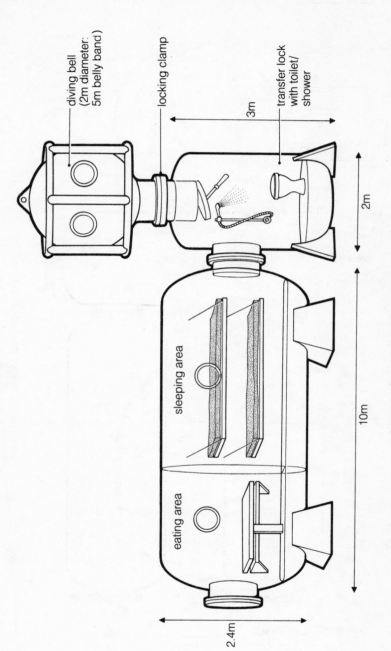

diving bell
(2m diameter:
5m belly band)

locking clamp

transfer lock
with toilet/
shower

3m

2m

sleeping area

eating area

10m

2.4m

Layout of saturation dive systems

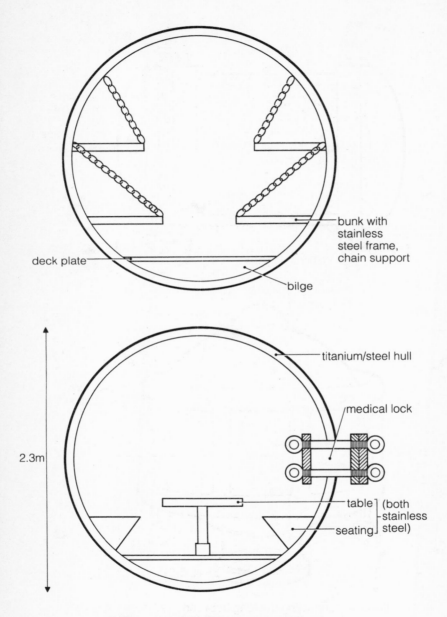

deck plate

bunk with
stainless
steel frame,
chain support

bilge

titanium/steel hull

medical lock

2.3m

table ⎤ (both
      ⎬ stainless
seating ⎦ steel)

Sectional view of sleeping area chamber *(above)*,
and eating area chamber *(below)*

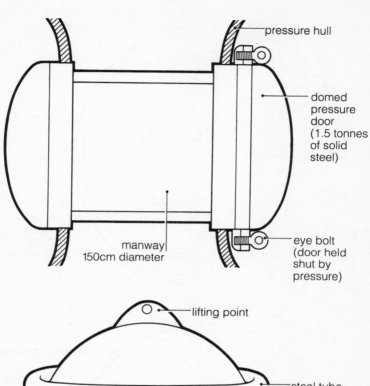

pressure hull

domed
pressure
door
(1.5 tonnes
of solid
steel)

eye bolt
(door held
shut by
pressure)

manway
150cm diameter

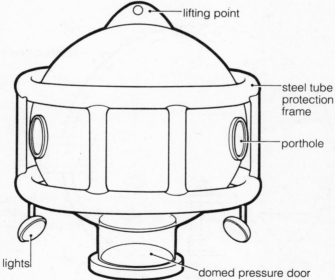

lifting point

steel tube
protection
frame

porthole

lights

domed pressure door

Detail of connecting trunking between chambers *(above)*,
and the diving bell *(below)*

1

Outside the steamed winter glass it was a splitting frost. Over each individual gravel chip of tarmac, winter had crystallised a diamond glaze. The yellow of the sodium lamps reflected back from the frozen edges of ridged willow bark. Up and down the road, light spilled yellow out of windows over small clots of cars butted in to the curb. Through the sensible suburban double-glazing there came the faint echo of music, canned memories from the sixties.

It was New Year's Eve in the winter of 1982 and there were a thousand more or less respectable parties going on in the suburbs. The party that we attended was respectable but not sedate. That was where it all started – drinking with Gerry on New Year's Eve. Gerry, who time and again plays a part in this account, was a North Sea diver from the very start, when they killed one man a month while the industry painfully groped its way through the development of a technology that allows men to do the most dangerous job in the world.

Even now, I'm still not certain who trained that generation of divers. Many of them were ex-Navy of course, or ex-SBS (Special Boat Service), refugees from the shadow world of covert military operations. Some of them, with enough to drink inside them, will give you a glimpse into those shadows now and then, but that New Year's Eve those brief confidences were a long way into the future.

It was, for me, a time not so much of crisis as profound unease. I was finished with teaching for a start. Teaching is a poor substitute for someone whose main interest is only in learning and, after twelve years of indifferent pay and poor conditions, I was ready to look for something fresh.

And there was Billy, of course. He was important too. God alone knows what he was doing there. Even Gerry knew better than to invite offshore friends to a party at home, but then, as I found out later, Billy Carson had no real home in the sense of a fixed base. He was the original oilfield gypsy. Everyone knew him, everyone respected him, and, right then, he didn't much like me.

Gerry on the other hand was actively recruiting me. He said, 'Why don't you be a Caisson Master?'

'A what?'

'Run the dive system, mix gas, monitor the divers, keep them alive. Maybe you would even get to be team medic. We always need medics.'

'But I don't dive. At least not since a few scuba dips and that was years ago.'

'You don't have to.'

'I don't even like to swim unless I have to.'

He looked at me blearily over a glass. 'The idea,' he said, 'is that you should sink.'

'Who can I contact about this crazy job?'

'Georges Arnoux at Comex Houlder.'

He gave me an address, and talked on. Pungent names peppered his descriptions, rich with the terminology of the frontier. Some of them American, from the days of the travelling carnivals who worked on wildcat drilling in the twenties, roustabouts, roughnecks. It was a whole new world.

Billy Carson wasn't so welcoming. He took me aside after Gerry had drifted off towards the dim lights of the kitchen, and the sweet, burning leaves smell of a joint making the rounds.

'Don't let him screw you up, laddie,' he said. 'It's not all glamour and bright lights out there. If you do this, it's twelve hours a day bloody hard graft, away from home six weeks at a stretch, and if you were to be a medic, the way he says, you'll be all there is between twenty good men and dying. They'll not forgive you if you screw up.'

He looked at me appraisingly as if I were some barely adequate tool that might just do a difficult job at a pinch. I was needled enough by his Dutch Uncle attitude to protest.

'I don't screw up,' I said.

'Well, not knowing you well enough to judge, maybe we'll see. But remember there's no bloody room for passengers out there, laddie.'

He got up and left for the toilet. It was an unpromising way to meet a man who was, in the end, to be as close to me as a brother, but right then I looked at his broad departing back and thought him middle-aged, embittered and a boor to boot.

Gerry's wife brought me another drink.

'Is he getting at you, Jon?' she asked.

'No, not really. I think he thinks the rest of the world doesn't understand him.'

'Perhaps they don't. Are you really going to go offshore?'

'I don't know. But I think so.'

She shook her head. 'God help you then.'

* * *

Weeks later I was reading about the mechanics of commercial diving.

It all comes down to pressure in the end. The sheer weight of water that squeezes a diver with a force of many tons as he goes deep. Years ago, even before deep dives were possible, they learned the effects of that pressure from tunnel workers.

Tunnels are pressurised too, to keep out the water in wet ground, and workers, returning quickly to the surface, suffered agonies of joint pains. Some were paralysed or died. At the turn of the century fashionable ladies affected a strange, contorted and supposedly elegant stance called the 'Grecian Bend'. The stricken workers, knotted into contorted shapes by the pains of decompression sickness, named their condition after them, hence 'the bends'.

And that is essentially the whole problem of deep diving. As you go deep, gases from the breathing mix dissolve in your blood. Release the pressure too fast and the bubbles that form cause pain. The answer of course is simply to release the pressure gently and Professor Haldane found how to do that fifty years ago, long before the North Sea fields were discovered.

But, in this area, one problem encapsulates another. The deeper you go the more gas dissolves in your body fluids. The more gas that dissolves, the longer it takes to clear it. Until, at North Sea depths, a man who works for an hour must decompress for fifteen hours or more. Economically ridiculous, and dangerous too, for repeated decompressions carry their own physical penalties. So once again, they found a solution.

If a man can live and work in a high-pressure atmosphere for days at a time, he will only need a single decompression. To achieve that one need only fabricate a steel container large enough to live in, that can be carried aboard a ship. Add to that idea a diving bell, to ride in from the pressure chamber to work on the seabed, and you have the beginnings of modern saturation diving and, of course, the need for a specialist to run the whole thing and that was the beginning of Caisson Masters.

So much for the theory. There are times and places when the practice is far from being so clear cut.

But it is not the intricate problems of survival that attract men into the industry, nor even the indecently high wage rates. There is something else too, the old call that my great-grandfather heard when he sailed from his terraced seaman's house in Falmouth and served as mate in the clipper trade around the world. His career filled the house and my childhood with half-understood echoes of the sea and the priceless junk that he had gathered from a hundred ports.

It is a familiar thing to the Cornish, the call of the sea. But I never thought to hear it.

*   *   *

Britain's divers are nowadays trained far from the North Sea oilfields in the calm, protected but icy cold waters of Loch Linnhe in the west of Scotland.

In the early days, when the North Sea construction boom started, they built a government training school in Fort William. Today it's a private organisation, a low ugly complex of buildings, jutting out into the waters of the loch. At the end of this jetty, isolated from the rest of the complex, is a rough shack full of gas bottles, and usually, moored alongside, a strange ungainly looking craft, no more than a floating platform holding a diving system. This is the training barge *Deep Diver One*.

After all the reading and the expectation, training is a culture shock. They understand divers at the Underwater Centre, understand them in fact all too well.

We don't start with diving. Life Support Technicians as they call us, in the British sector (the vivid term 'Caisson Master' is used today only by the poetic French at Comex), start with calculations involving gas. Volumes of gas, cylinders of gas, gas temperatures, gas handling, gas pumping, gas system fittings. They leave you in no doubt that there is a great deal to learn before they let you aboard that barge. There is even more to learn before they actually let you near a diver.

The first day, the first lecture, the very first thing that they say to you is not 'Good morning' but, 'A superquad of Heliox Mix contains

200 bar. How much gas is available from it?' And when you work up the nerve to ask what the hell a superquad is (it's a rack of sixty-four gas cylinders), they complicate it again and again and again.

Later we found out why. It's because of yet another problem, with yet another exotic solution. When you breathe air it doesn't just dissolve in your blood. Nitrogen, of which air is mostly made up, acts just like any other inert gas at pressure, in other words it's anaesthetic. The French, still the poets of the industry, call the resulting dangerous euphoria and lack of co-ordination 'Raptures of the Deep'. We British call it 'Nitrogen Narcosis' or even less poetically 'the Narcs'.

And so in deep diving, we don't use air. Instead we use lighter, simpler gases. In theory we could use hydrogen, the lightest of all, but it explodes with air, and escapes from tiny holes to lay a lethal trap for the unwary. So instead we use helium, at thirty-five dollars a cubic foot, and that astonishing price, currently some four hundred pounds a cylinder, is why we worry about the gas.

Helium does have one other side effect too, as every schoolkid who has sucked the Heligas from a balloon knows very well. Breathe a little helium and you sound like an irritable Donald Duck. Breathe a lot and you hardly sound at all, and that doesn't help communication.

They told us horror stories too at Fort William and there are horrors enough from the early days of the industry and even from more recent times. They talk about the drilling rig *Byford Dolphin* where a clamp holding a pressure door failed for reasons that were never fully explained. The blast of gas killed eight men, divers and surface crew alike.

They tell you of the strange and terrible case of Daniel Webster who was peacefully sitting on the toilet inside the pressurised system when somehow, the flush valve opened sealing him neatly to the bowl and holding him there with the gas pressure ripping out half his large intestine like the world's largest and cruellest vacuum cleaner. Despite all the odds, he survived to fight another day.

They show you pictures too, of men from the old standard dress days when divers wore a copper dome hard hat and a waterproofed canvas suit. And they show what happened when the non-return valve failed and the water pressure tried to force the flexible suit, and the man inside it, back into the incompressible dome of the hat. Strange how small a volume a human body can occupy.

Finally, after ten days of theory had convinced all the candidates that the job was hard, exacting and dangerous we were trooped out to *Deep Diver One* to try out the theory in practice.

That very first saturation dive was, looking back, very simple. We had an instructor with us the whole time for a start, sitting there ready to step in and remind us before things went irretrievably wrong. Of course we all of us hoped that he wouldn't too often but there's no doubt that his presence was immensely reassuring. It needed to be of course. Inside three cylinders twenty feet long by seven in diameter there would be six divers. It was their first time too, though most of them had dived on air commercially before they came to take this course and they knew the score.

At first sight the control panel of a saturation diving system is a nightmare. On a simple panel like the *Deep Diver One* there are a hundred odd valves of all sizes and colours, sixty gauges, seven TV monitor screens, eight analysers for oxygen, eight for carbon dioxide, three communications links with helium unscramblers that are supposed to eliminate the squeaky helium voice but don't, and a whole range of odd extras.

We took it in turns to go over the panel checking valve by valve, pressurising the system on air, checking the gas storage, climbing over the great blue painted bulk of the chambers to examine lights and cameras and trace the maze of bright painted tubes that carried gases in and out of them.

Finally the divers arrived. All young, all fresh faced, all trying to pretend that this was just routine, that they'd done it a thousand times before, but they hadn't and nor had we. The trouble was that they also knew how inexperienced the topside crew were and that is a situation that is apt to make them nervous.

They trooped into the chamber area, each man with a soft bag of clothes and personal gear. This was to be a short saturation, only five days from closing the doors to opening them, but the routine is the same as for the twenty-eight to thirty days that they will spend in 'sat' in the North Sea. We checked each bag and each man for prohibited items. Innocent things can be nasty under pressure. Aerosols, sealed bottles of aftershave, lighters, all of them can absorb gas under pressure to burst later as they come out of the system. All divers know the rules but we always check them anyway. It was not beyond the instructors to plant a prohibited item to test us out. Anything that is airtight might collapse under pressure on the way down so that jars of coffee and bottles of condiments are opened before we start. Things are even worse on the way back up, the implosion of a bottle of ketchup is messy, its explosion can have splinters of glass whistling through the air like shrapnel.

When we were satisfied that everything was as it should be, everyone gathered in the control room, even the half of the course who would take over at midnight to cover the twelve hours of the night shift. No one wanted to be the first to move. The instructor had seen it all before. He opened communication to the divers.

'Hello, inside.'

'Hello.'

'We're ready if you are?'

'OK.' (They did sound nervous.)

'We'll take you to fifteen feet depth and stop for a leak check, OK?'

'Roger that.'

He turned to the four of us.

'Right, who's supervisor this shift?'

We had drawn lots for this earlier.

'I am,' I said, wishing I wasn't.

'OK. Let's get them down.'

The gas was on line already, all I had to do was open one single valve, but it was still a relief to see the gauge creep steadily down past five feet to ten and then to fifteen where I stopped and called the divers.

'Hello, inside.'

'Yeah. Hello.'

'Right, that's you at fifteen feet depth – we're checking system integrity.'

'OK.' They sounded relieved that it was under way. I certainly was.

The other three checked the system for escaping gas, squirting each possible source of leakage with detergent solution from a squeezy bottle. This low-tech equipment often detects escapes too small to detect by ear. The leak blows bubbles. We would notice it on the gauges but we check just the same. I stayed at the panel. The rule here is simple. As long as there are men in the system the panel is watched day and night. It's never ever left, not even for a moment. If there is an emergency the split-second decision that is all the time we have to correct a situation is in the hands of the

man on the panel. If he should fail to make the right decision it is
his responsibility to explain his actions to the inquiry afterwards.

You go through endless checklists both before and during a
saturation. It may be boring but no one can afford to rely on
memory. As they reached depth things relaxed. Talking to the
divers was harder now as the voice distortion became extreme.

The chambers are warm, damp and clammy inside, but that is
another problem with an odd solution. Helium acts almost as if it
were a liquid metal at depth, stripping the heat out of the divers'
bodies with every breath that they take. The margin of tolerance is
narrow, and narrower as we increase depth. At three hundred feet
the temperature can vary only by a couple of degrees. But divers
constantly call for adjustments, up a degree, down a degree. In
the end we told them the adjustment was made but worked to
our surface gauges. Much of this contact with the surface team
is just for reassurance. On actual jobs the men in the chambers
will sometimes swap gossip for an hour at a time with the surface,
simply for the sake of talking to someone in the safe world outside
their steel shell.

While we were pressurising the system the barge was towed out
to the centre of the loch. Below us in the darkness was a sunken
steel-hulled tug, a wooden work boat and a steel frame made of
pipes and tubes and girders to practise inspection on. As soon as
we were over it the first two divers were transferred to the bell for
the trip to the bottom.

The bell is a sphere of steel with strong water and airtight doors to
seal it. We clamped it on to the pressure chambers and pumped gas
into it until its pressure matched the depth in the system. If there is
a weak point in saturation diving it is here at these vital pressure
hull doors. On our first time it went well, everyone remembered the
stages of the complex drill. We talked to each other all the time on
deck radios, with the man on the panel in charge.

The days of the saturation passed quickly. Twelve-hour shifts
leave you tired out and there is little time for anything but work
and sleep. Then quite suddenly it was the day of the exam. We had
all heard on the grapevine that this was a very difficult test to fail but
we did not want to be the exception that proves this amiable rule. No
candidate who scores less than seventy per cent gets a certificate and
a green logbook. All our group passed. Now all we needed was 200
days' offshore experience before a second and final exam and then

we would be allowed to do for real the things that we had practised that week. Under the Association of Offshore Contractors' rules we would be qualified to take the industry by storm.

We celebrated in the Crofter's Arms in Fort William, for us the first of a whole series of diving industry pubs all round the world. In time their names and locations would become familiar – the Dickens in Stavanger, the Three Musketeers in Amsterdam, the Beachcomber in Warri, the Station Bar in Haugesaund and a hundred more. It's still a tiny industry where a man is only as good as his last job and before long each of us would be able to walk on to a work site anywhere in the world and be greeted by a friend.

The Underwater Centre gave us a list of all the diving companies they knew of. They sounded exotic, with addresses in Malaysia, Singapore, Warri, Point Noire, Los Angeles. But we were advised to work on less fanciful destinations. 'Concentrate on Aberdeen and Yarmouth,' the instructor told us. 'They have big jobs under British rules and they need Assistant LSTs.'

LSTs are Life Support Technicians, the industry's catch-all label for the men whose job it is to run the diving systems. Of course he didn't tell us that the oil price slide had destroyed the old free and easy market of yesterday or that a good half of that long list of companies had gone to the wall. There was however one last complication. You need to have done a survival course. You can't work in the North Sea without it.

* * *

'Survival at Sea and Firefighting' is taught with varying degrees of efficiency by a scattered handful of disparate schools, tech colleges and offshore training centres through the country.

For three days we sweated across a fireground in rough heavy-weight fire-brigade serge while they taught us how to put out fires, breathe with compressed air sets and to smoke dive into pitch-black mazes full of foul-smelling cosmetic smoke to find a weighted and stuffed body by feel alone. The training is uncomfortable, difficult and nasty. The reality on the other hand is simple terror. Perhaps it's true that there can be no adequate training for an oilfield fire at sea, but the course gave us some confidence and perhaps that was enough.

From fire we transferred our attentions to water. Training drill in echoing swimming pools after hours, wrestling life-rafts upright while the lights flickered to confuse, leaping in life jackets from the ten-metre board all the while remembering to hold the jacket down, remembering the instructor's casual warning, 'Jump in wrong, lads, and it'll thump you in the balls.'

It does too.

Then there was the dunker. If a helicopter goes into the water the first thing it will do is turn upside down. So they strap you in a crude mock-up of a helicopter, plunge you three at a time into twenty feet of water and then turn you upside down to give you an idea of what it feels like. It is not an activity designed to appeal to any but a masochist.

After this, with yet another certificate safely filed away, I felt that I was ready. By now we were well into the winter of 1983–4 and I needed to show a return on the massive investment of time and energy that the diving industry had cost me. Gerry, my long-time friend and mentor, back from a lucrative trip to the Gulf on war zone pay, was sympathetic but implacable.

'You still need the Medics' Course,' he said, sipping from a glass of duty-free rum.

'I can't really afford it.'

'It's a waste not to, after all you've done so far. Look, take the course at Yarmouth, and then give yourself a few weeks in casualty here. You know the boss, don't you?'

In fact the local casualty consultant is an old friend.

'Yes, but . . .'

'Have a rum and think about it.'

Of course by the time I actually got into casualty things were different.

Three weeks at the North Sea Medical Unit had taught me a little, just a little, about what the job involved. Better than that, I had finally discovered what it was I wanted to spend the next few years of my life doing.

2

The pace of the medics' training is relentless, first lectures are at eight thirty in the morning and evening sessions last far into the night, but the practical relevance of the course and the fact that it is all taught by men who have been there and done it for real, makes it intensely interesting.

Much of the material was diving related, treatment for gas embolus, treatment for decompression sickness. But sutures and drips? And an epileptic who was previously unsuspected and who came in fitting every three minutes while half a dozen staff and students tried to get a dose of Valium into his rectum?

Casualty is where the realities of the job finally get to you. Fully half of all trainees quit at that point. All the theory, all the fine fellow feeling takes a hard knock the first time a fatal RTA (road traffic accident) comes through the door. Still it is the best part of the training. No one ever forgets the first time that you function as a medic, the first few faltering attempts to understand a real live patient.

My first two nights were observation only. On the second night, three hours into a particularly short-staffed, overstretched Saturday night shift, an old man was brought in dead. I offered to help the porter trundle the long stainless steel box down to the morgue. Now this should surely have been within my capabilities. We got lost. Complete with the corpse we wandered the night-time labyrinth of the hospital. It was the porter's first night too and he had no more idea where the morgue was than I had. Finally we were rescued by a tall Indian sister who we met walking the corridors in the depths of the hospital wearing a traditional full-length cloak.

My first actual patient was a belligerent drunk who had walked along the street outside punching out windows. His hands were full of glass splinters and despite two policemen holding him down he was still fighting drunk. I went into the cubicle with a tutor nurse, and two huge porters. The drunk eyed us.

'I'll ha' the bloody lot o' yus.'

One of the policemen shook his head. 'Don't bother trying to talk him out of it. Just tell us how you want him held down.'

They turned him face down with his head to one side on the couch. I needed him held this way in case he should vomit and choke. His hands were cuffed behind him. There were four major cuts, all gaping, wet and red. But the houseman who had checked him said that there was no tendon damage, he just needed skin sutures.

I swabbed the stainless steel top of the trolley and opened the suture pack. Gloves on first. Not only to protect the patient but to protect us too. No one wants to risk HIV or hepatitis. The drunk eyed the 25 ml bottle of lignocaine.

'You'se not sticking me with that stuff.'

The tutor nurse smiled sweetly and said, 'Well, if you would prefer treatment without the anaesthetic, or perhaps you would rather discharge yourself and bleed to death outside?'

She said it in a voice of sweet reason that carried long years of experience in handling drunks. The drunk subsided. I put the injections low on the wrist, intending to flood the radial and ulnar nerves and kill sensation right through the affected hand. We waited five minutes by the clock.

As soon as I went near the drunk with the needle holder, barely even pressing on the skin, he started to scream and shout.

'Jesus that hurts. That stuff doesn't work I tell you.'

I put the needle down and put three infiltration injections into the wounds themselves. That should have been enough to amputate his hand never mind stitch a few cuts.

Once again as soon as I touched his skin he yelled out.

I moved to the table again and as I did his eyes followed me. The tutor nurse deftly slipped a stay stitch into the first wound. The patient was unaware of it.

She said, 'Now. Perhaps if the acting is finished for the night we can close these cuts.'

I stitched, feeling the eyes of the policemen watching each move. I don't know who was more nervous, me or the patient. Inside the rubber gloves the french chalk was sticky from sweat. Altogether I put in twenty-three stitches. Finally I stepped back.

The wounds were red lines crossed by the black ties of the Ethilon sutures. Along each one was a neat line of knots. I dressed the hand, spraying the wound with Providone Iodine to sterilise it. Gauze and clinical white bandage covered the job.

The policemen dragged my patient back out to the waiting van. Throughout there was not a single sentence from the man that was not abusive.

My tutor took me for a coffee.

'That wasn't bad. But next time try to tie all the knots to one side. It looks better and it's easier when you take the sutures out. Also try to remember that some of them think they can feel pain even when they can't. If you've given the right dose of lignocaine, test it before you give more. Otherwise pretty good.'

High praise indeed.

Outside a blue lamp went past. Contrary to popular belief ambulance drivers only use the blue lights if they have a rush job on board. It gives the reception staff a vital few seconds more. We heard from the others waiting by the doors that the incoming case was an arterial bleeder, an attempted suicide.

He was perhaps thirty and fair haired and very very pale when they got him into reception and on to a trolley. The ambulance staff had already intubated him and he was on oxygen forcing a little extra carrying capacity out of his bloodstream, whatever was left of it. His clothes were soaked in blood and his arms were swathed up to the elbows in white gauze. Patients whose clothes are soaked that way are often bleeding very badly indeed, a serious attempt at suicide rather than a Saturday night drunken self-pity session.

The call went for the surgical registrar as he might need surgical repair, also for the medical reg to assess him. In the meanwhile we needed a route into his veins. There was a pulse, faint and far away like a drumbeat from a distant shore, but his blood pressure was so low that we could hardly register it.

There was nowhere to put a needle into his arm but eventually it slipped into his leg. We had three units of plasma expander ready for him, until his blood was cross-matched, that was the best we could do. The team worked smoothly and quickly, hardly saying a word while I concentrated on staying out of the way, and learning.

Twenty minutes after admission his pulse was stronger and his blood pressure was returning. Meanwhile the medical reg had arrived.

'Right,' he said, 'we'll have the dressings off and assess the damage. Donald's tied up in theatre for at least three hours, so we best get on with it.'

The dressings were progressively more blood-soaked. Returning pressure had restarted the bleeding.

'All of you. Aprons and gloves, please.'

We put on disposable plastic aprons as he gingerly lifted the dressing on the right wrist. He shook his head and beckoned me to look.

'Determined bugger.'

The cuts were roughly T-shaped, one directly across the wrist, one at right angles up the inner aspect of the arm towards the elbow. They were gaping a good deal and muscle and tendon glistened there.

'Right, this is a surgical job. We'll cover up for now and get the Ortho man to look. There are at least three tendons cut there, maybe more. It's a mess.'

He bound the remains of the arm, and left. Presently the patient, still comatose but stable at last, was taken away.

Later, a matter of some weeks, we were told the outcome. The patient went through reconstruction of his arms perfectly but died while under observation later. At the post-mortem they found that, as well as the slashed wrists, he had swallowed most of a packet of paraquat. A very determined bugger indeed.

In time everything becomes routine, and that can happen surprisingly quickly. After ten days of casualty work the constant flow of accident cases is no longer daunting. You quickly get over wondering if you might faint, quickly learn where supplies are stored, becoming, even in that short time, an accepted part of the hospital scene. It makes for a comforting sense of support that will be wholly absent on actual emergencies at sea.

In the hospital there are a hundred experienced shoulders to lean on if things get bad. Above all, the final responsibility of the decision is elsewhere. Offshore the only link with help is by radio and it is all too easy to filter the information that you pass back to the base, colouring descriptions a shade to fit your own preconceived diagnosis.

They gave us a flavour of the realities on the Medics' Course, turning us three at a time into a large room containing a faked accident complete with multiple casualties, fake blood, simulated groans and screams and, tucked away behind a pile of oil drums, a victim who quietly bleeds to death while you are involved elsewhere. In training all there is to lose are a few points on the assessment.

At some point, with luck, you go out on the ambulances to accident scenes. It's during this time that you realise that it's true that Accident and Emergency staff are addicted to their own adrenalin.

In the rest room between calls the crews tell newcomers about especially difficult or gory accidents that they have handled. Most of this is the real stuff, honest advice that is worth its weight in pure gold when the time comes. A few of the stories are there to test you. It's a harmless game but played in dead earnest to an extent, because the man or woman who cannot be trusted to react properly could endanger the whole team in the heat of the moment.

The first night out happened to be a Saturday. We lurked, tucked into the shadows of the city-centre back streets monitoring the radio. Calls to other units crackled across frequently and it seemed that ours was the only quiet sector. Then finally the call came, to a disturbance in a pub, three injured, police already in attendance. We got there very quickly, blue lights reflecting back off the windows of the stores, siren whooping echoes in the concrete valleys. Up ahead there was a knot of blue lights gathered. We pulled in and the crowd separated to let us through. The regular crew were in dayglo and to avoid confusion I was still wearing a white coat. The police took it as a badge of authority.

The young policeman who greeted us was pale and tense, voice up an octave with excitement. He said, 'We've two bad ones. One glassing, one knife wound, and a minor injury. He was out cold but he seems OK now.'

The inside of the pub was bright lit, littered with unfinished drinks and still hazed with smoke. The stab wound was sitting against the bar on the floor. His chest was wet red from three inches below the left collar bone. The others took the glass wound, a young man whose face was a mask of blood and who sat sobbing. The tears cut diluted pinkish tracks down his cheeks.

The man with the stab wound was maybe eighteen, maybe younger. He tried to grin as I knelt beside him.

I said, 'OK, mate, just relax. I'm going to take a quick look, put a dressing on that and then we'll get you to hospital.'

Under his shirt the wound was short, deep, and gaping. There were pinkish bubbles around it. This was a sucking chest wound. I knew that from theory. Air was getting drawn into the hole in his chest each time he breathed in. In the end, if it wasn't stopped, his lungs would collapse in a bilateral pneumothorax.

I knew the theory and still I was stuck looking at that small gaping bloody slit between his ribs.

The ambulance driver came over.

'What have we got?'

'Sucking chest.'

'OK, I'll show a good trick they taught me in the army.'

He took a three-inch square of polythene out of his kit and taped it close against the skin so that the lower side was open, and three of the sides were sealed.

As I watched the makeshift valve fluttered to allow air out and, as the patient inhaled, sucked tight and sealed in the blood over the wound. He grinned. 'Who needs the Heimlich valve, eh? It works best with a condom but the lubricant makes it difficult to get the tape to stick.'

The patient grinned, looked down at his chest and then, quite suddenly, vomited on the carpet.

We had no sooner run them to casualty, completed the clean-up and checked the paperwork when another call came. This time it was an RTA. An Escort with four people in it had hit a truck head on.

We sliced through the traffic, sirens howling and blue lights flashing, engine not muted now, but belting out the power, with the great heavy, soft sprung body rolling from side to side.

The traffic was well backed up from the crash site which was on a dual carriageway section on the outskirts of the city. We weaved through narrow gaps, rumbling over grass central reservations, ploughing through the council's bright flowerbeds.

The truck was mangled to rough metal strips, paint torn off, chrome crushed, primer showing dirty grey through the pale blue of the paintwork. A fire rescue tender was already there and they were manhandling hydraulic tongs to cut the pillars of the roof. The truck was so damaged that there was no possibility of anyone crawling in to assess the people inside, but through the smashed glass, we could see that the driver was dead, and the others were at least unconscious. There was a smell of spilled oil in the air, somehow I had expected it to be petrol.

The fire brigade lifted the roof section clear and propped the truck body with steel jacks. We moved in. The ambulance driver was in the back of the car, calling to us.

'Right-hand one is gone. Chest injury. I think this one . . . Right, I've got a pulse.'

We concentrated on the broken body. It was a woman aged fifty or so with a bright evening dress, flecked with Lurex threads, and splattered with someone's blood. We had to take care in lifting her. There are so many possibilities, from spinal injury to sharp jagged rib splinters lurking like hidden traps inside her chest. At least she was unconscious, she'd feel nothing. We slipped a hard collar around her neck to stabilise her upper spine, and they had to tear off the door so that we could get her clear. The fireman who ripped it away attacked the metal like an enemy.

As we stabilised her on the stretcher her eyes opened. Most people are disoriented and deeply shocked at that point. But she turned her pale blood-stained, middle-aged face to look at the wreck and saw a fireman covering what was left of the driver. A single tear cut through the dirt and blood and makeup on her face. She lay there in the open, lit by the blue beacons and the fire-brigade floodlights, surrounded by strangers. Everybody's aunty in a cheap evening dress trying to come to terms with sudden violent death.

By now a second ambulance crew was on the scene and because they were better placed to get clear quickly, they took the woman. We had to wait at the scene for one of our doctors to certify death.

The other backseat passenger, the woman's husband maybe, was dead, cold to the touch already, but still with the supple relaxed muscles of living flesh. The driver and front-seat passenger were crushed beyond hope. There was a steady ticking of cooling metal from somewhere.

On the way back to the hospital we saw a man sitting with both legs in the gutter in front of him, singing. He flagged us down. We were not supposed to stop for drunks, but we pulled up anyway. When he tried to stand, he promptly fell on his arse in the gutter, his right ankle at an angle of ninety degrees to his leg.

'It's me sodding ankle,' said the drunk by way of explanation.

The driver looked at it askance. 'I can see that,' he said. 'You just wait there while we get a stretcher.'

'I don't need that. Open the doors.'

We did. To get the stretcher. And before anyone could stop him the drunk climbed aboard, broken ankle and all, and sat there with a big sloppy grin on his face.

'See?' he said in a voice of triumph.

On the way in he took a bottle out of his pocket and swigged at it. He shouldn't really have been allowed to drink in case they needed to use a general anaesthetic on him later, but considering the state of him I didn't feel disposed to argue.

He sang all the way in. Actually he'd got a good voice. He sang non-stop while they set his leg, too, and stood it all without a murmur. Anaesthesia, beyond that already self-administered, was not required.

*   *   *

Training in casualty passed all too quickly, partly because there was great satisfaction in working there, partly because there was too much to learn in so short a time. The last few days were part of the run-up to Christmas and the treatment area was bright with tinsel bells and complex geometric forms that reflected the hard white lights.

The drunks, injured, abusive and just plain incapable, suffered a brief but spectacular rise in frequency.

On my last shift everyone gathered in the coffee room to say goodbye. My chosen career was viewed with some awe by the nurses, even the tough casualty sisters had misgivings, though whether on my account or that of my future patients I could not decide.

Someone said, 'You'll be by yourself out there, no back-up?'

'Only telemetry and radio.'

'No X-rays?'

'No.'

'No lab. No whole blood?'

'Just saline and plasma expanders.'

'Good luck.'

It set the tone for a good many such goodbyes, and the brief egocentric glow that comes from knowing that this is a very special job and, as such, is respected even by the professionals who have seen it all. I suppose the gladiators always felt that way, too, and of course it's pure foolishness. The reality was to be much, much tougher than that.

3

The time that followed initial training was probably the most frustrating of all. By now it was the summer of 1984 and the oil price had collapsed from a five-year peak to an extent that made marginally profitable fields no longer viable.

All over the world oil workers waited on the beach for the phone calls that usually start the diving season. There is a set scale of pay but up until then it was customary to negotiate for each job above the minimum. We had been told that for a job in mid-summer we could expect to go above the ninety-three pounds a day minimum to around the hundred and five mark. If the call ever came.

The days grew longer. I took odd dive related work with civil companies. These are the inshore diving operators who service docks and canals and some shallow water offshore work. It was not what I had trained for.

There is great isolation in unemployment especially in the offshore industry. Because we are free to live where we will, working on sites offshore as required, a team may well be scattered all over the country. There are pockets of concentration of course, one around Aberdeen, another one around Hull, but at that stage I only knew one man in the industry that I could talk to and Gerry bore the brunt of my doubts.

He was sure that it would pick up.

'After all,' he said, 'with your qualifications they should be pleased to get you.'

'Sure. But no one is working right now.'

'Have you tried Comex?'

'Yes. They've a single site and it's fully crewed.'

'2Ws?'

'Nothing.'

'Svitzer?'

'No.'

'OK.' He picked up the phone and dialled a number.

There were many long days like that, when we spent time ringing around, sometimes together, sometimes separately, running through the list of active companies, picking up rumours, following up possibilities. Always it was the same story. Recession, low oil prices and no jobs active.

Finally, when I was sure that there was no choice but to cast around for something else, the phone rang. An unfamiliar female voice said, 'This is BUE diving. Are you available for work next week?'

'Yes. Yes, of course.'

'All right. It's a Hereema barge, the *Hermod*. The job is construction in Norway. Up to three weeks' diving.'

'Great.'

'You are a qualified medic as well as an LST?'

'Yes.'

'Good. We need a team medic as well. Will you cover that too?'

'Certainly.'

'I'll get back to you as soon as we have details.'

There followed a period of nervous anticipation. To some going to sea to start a job is a challenge to be welcomed, but to me, because it means leaving home and family, there is always a time of reflection before each departure. Offshore workers have one of the highest rates of marriage breakdown in the country. Long periods away, the risks and the tendency of many to find comfort in a bottle between trips, coupled with a great deal of cash, all conspire to destroy relationships. Taking on the diving industry was not just a personal challenge. At home there were long, sometimes nervous discussions about the risks, financial and personal. Few women willingly accept their men choosing to work in an environment that routinely includes real hazards. But we talked it through, decided that there could never be gains without risks, and from there on the certainty of my wife's support was a fixed point in a career where everything else was in the habit of sudden change.

Gerry, who knew and understood the strains, had no concrete advice for once, though he did have one small piece of information, the boss of the job that I was joining was Billy Carson.

'You see?' said Gerry. 'I told you the old bugger liked you.'

To reach Aberdeen meant taking the late train through the night to arrive at six in the morning. The station was cold and smelled of old oil and urine and stone. It was a lovely sunset. There were a few men scattered around waiting for the connection to Manchester. Later I came to know most of them by sight and a few became close friends, but then each man seemed to stand alone.

Preston at three in the morning. One of the hubs of the rail network. A single buffet stays open through the night serving styrofoam coffee and microwaved bacon rolls. More men stood waiting on the platform.

This was the oilman's special, the overnight mail to the oil capital of the UK, one of the few long-distance trains with no buffet, no bar, and room for all the passengers to sit. I found a double seat to lie across. Later I could afford a sleeper, but on that first trip such luxury was outside my reach.

Aberdeen station at six in the morning, men stretching away the aches of the night before, bright sunlight and yellow sandstone, bright minibuses picking up and disgorging crews. I noticed names familiar only from books, Odeco, BP Exploration, Scot Catering, Marathon Petroleum. Aberdeen never leaves you in any doubt that this is a city whose lifeblood is North Sea crude.

We didn't have a crewbus or if we did I had no idea where to find it. So I made my leisurely way to the heliport and the British Caledonian desk. There was plenty of time, four hours before the passenger lists were finally delivered from the company and seven or more before the flight. I watched the helicopters flutter off, and come in to land, disgorging men in bright orange rubberised survival suits. Though I had expected all of it, the reality was hard to grasp. It was like seeing a great national monument or a work of art for the first time.

Eventually another man came in for the BUE job. Broad-set, relaxed and friendly, he was George Patterson, dive supervisor on this job and my immediate boss.

He knew it was the first time for me and went out of his way to make me feel at home. Others rolled in, in quick succession, and we all decided to visit the office which I learnt is a dive team ritual. Whenever a team finds itself in Aberdeen with nothing but time, stuck at a heliport or fogged in at the Skean Dhu Hotel, they tend to visit the people who are otherwise just voices on a phone. Dive teams enjoy these visits. The office staff do not. We also tried to extract what we could from stores. Overalls, two pairs to each man, workboots, gloves, hard hat. There were more introductions, by now there had been too many names, too many people.

The helicopter was delayed of course. But George was relaxed about the delay. As he explained, we were, after all, on pay at that point.

Finally we were ushered through security, a baggage search and a quick pat down. Alcohol is strictly forbidden offshore and smuggling is a serious matter. We entered a corridor with a serving hatch to one side. A man was issuing survival suits, summing each of us up in a second before selecting the appropriate size.

The suit is rubberised and waterproof. Zipped up it will keep you alive in the winter North Sea for ten hours or so but only if the seals at wrist and neck keep the cold water out. Each of us checked the seals. The TV screen in front of us blared a quick burst of martial sounding music and a logo flashed up on the screen. Most of the men ignored it and read or smoked, suit zips down to the waist to stay cool, the orange fabric gathered around their hips. The video gave the impression that every second helicopter was likely to ditch and told you what to do in the event.

Actually the helicopter system is very safe, few go down and of those that do most float and the evacuation is simple. Still, there were a lot of men who were nervous of the flight.

That first helicopter was a Super Puma and by most standards it was cramped. We packed into the cabin in our suits and put on the headphones that allowed communication and drowned out the racket of the rotors.

The pilot came on the line. It was two hours' flying time to the *Hermod*, at present under way in the Norwegian sector. We settled in. He brought the machine to a hover ten feet above the tarmac and then we were off into the blue with the bright sun ticking off the pool of rotors above us.

*   *   *

Semi-Submersible Crane Vessel *Hermod* was one of the largest man-made structures ever to float. Essentially no more than a steel platform floating on two submerged pontoons, she served as a working base for two massive cranes.

From the air as we approached the barge it was those cranes that dominated the first impression. Because she was under tow, fussed around by a couple of attendant Hereema tugs, both cranes were in a fully down position, lying along the cradles on the deck. From the air the spiderwork of steel that made up the booms seemed far too delicate for the 5,000 metric tonnes that each crane could lift.

We went to the hover and settled with a gentle bump on my first offshore installation. I was assigned to the night shift and in that I was lucky. Nights are the quiet time offshore. Few of the management staff are about for fully three quarters of the shift. Crews on nights are free to work their own way.

The two LSTs I was with were both experienced and highly skilled, relaxed professionals who were the best possible example to learn from.

The first stage of any diving operation is to take stock of the gas available and to hook up the long flexible plastic tubes ('gas whips' in the trade) to the distribution panel. On all construction barges deck space is at a premium and, because gas cylinders are bulky, the deck crew always stack racks of gas as high as they safely can. That first night we climbed over these piles running the whips across the steel cages and tying them off at each available point of contact with the steelwork. If a whip should burst a free length of hose will saw back and forth through the air with all the force of 3,000 pounds to the square inch behind it. The ties are supposed to restrict the movement of the tubing enough to let us reach a valve to turn off the supply.

It was a strange introduction to the job, climbing high above the brightly lit deck to pass the stiff coils of synflex across the top of the racks. Looking out from there the deck was all light and shadow, stripped of colour by the Mercury lamps' blue glare that washed out the high northern twilight.

Late on, on the first shift just as the sun started to climb back from the lowest point on the horizon, the Oseburg B jacket arrived on its barge. A jacket is a huge spidery steel frame that sits on the bottom of the ocean with steel decking and the various working parts of the platform on top of it.

These structures are truly titanic, perhaps three hundred feet high when upright and two hundred across the base. When they arrive on site they are literally tipped off the barge that brings them, and sunk precisely into place by flooding various tanks that are part of the structure.

This is of course a delicate process and it can go quite horribly wrong. From the site of operations we could still see the aftermath of just such a mishap. There a jacket had been sunk to its design depth and had come to rest just three feet above the surface of the sea, instead of the intended seventy or so. Once in place it was of course unsalvable and there it remains, tenanted only by the seabirds, marked for ever by a light beacon as one of the truly colossal engineering errors of the oil industry.

Nothing however went wrong on this occasion. The Oseburg B jacket floated gently to her intended destination and sank almost imperceptibly slowly into position. When the engineers checked the base to be sure of its orientation we found that the structure was within an inch of the ideal position.

We gathered our team in the chambers, checked through the endless pre-blowdown lists, and pressurised eight men to a sat depth of 300 metres. At that depth it would take four days and twenty hours to recover them back to the surface.

We were well into the job when I finally learned what being an offshore medic is all about. It was late in the night shift but still of course, being Norway in summer, quite light when the call came.

We had already had one bit of excitement that night when the rig medic had been called to help a desperately injured man on a nearby trawler. The condition of this casualty was such that he needed escort to the beach and so, under the terms of our diving contract, the dive team medic took over cover of the barge crew's medical needs until he should get back.

Billy Carson came into the control room about three in the morning. Addressing me directly for the first time in days he said, 'Right, Jon. Got a job for you. One of the Spaniards has hurt himself. They need you to look him over.'

Most of the fabrication crew were Basques from the shipyards around San Sebastian.

I said, 'Where is he?'

'Yeah well, that's the problem. He's on the Port Crane.'

'On it?'

'Halfway up the jib.'

'I'll get the gear from the hospital.'

'Right. Quick as you can then. There's a panic on, you know.'

The hospital was in the control tower at the far end of the barge three storeys above working deck level. So I walked the length of the football-field sized deck through the bore of one of the steel piles stacked ready for use. This is not as eccentric as it sounds, as the huge steel tubes offer a safe covered walkway against lumps of falling metal, welding sparks, and other debris and of course they are clear underfoot.

From the hospital window I could see the Port Crane towering over me. It had been in use earlier in the day to lift piles out to the jacket and when that phase of the job had been taken over by the Starboard Crane, the Port had been left at forty-five degrees of tilt for routine maintenance. Its base, where the spidery steel lattice of the jib joined the tub of the roundhouse containing the engines, was eighty feet above the deck. Its far end, where the pulley wheel caught a brief pont of light in the sky, was at least three times that.

There is a walkway along the lower side of the boom of these big cranes. It is open steelwork and there are no safety barriers. At the base of the crane Cesario the deck foreman was waiting. He did speak English but with a combination of Spanish grammar and English curses that was quite unique.

'OK, English,' he said, grinning his white teeth out of a face the texture of leather, 'are you ready to be a fucking rigger?'

'As ready as I'll ever be.'

'OK. He's about three parts of the way along the boom.'

(That was at least a hundred and eighty feet above the water.)

'OK.'

'Right. So we climb the bloody crane, yes?'

He started up the ladder that led up towards the base of the boom. This one was easy, simple steel rungs with a cage around it to protect it but, even so, climbing with the emergency kit was awkward. We reached the base of the boom. It rose in a dead straight line in front of us, canted at a steep angle and narrowed to a point at the far end. It was nothing to Cesario.

He said, 'OK. When you walk along the bloody boom you just put one foot in front of another, yes? You don't bloody look down. If you want, clip yourself to the steel. You want a belt of karabiners?'

He offered me a leather belt with perhaps fifty spring clips on it which can be clipped on to a safety rope. It will not stop a trip but it will hold your fall after ten feet or so.

I took the belt and strapped it on.

'OK. We go, yes?'

Cesario strolled along the boom as if it was a pavement. I followed, much more slowly, gingerly clipping a safety line every few feet.

Cesario grinned. 'Don't worry about the bloody drop. After fifteen metres or so it doesn't matter.' And he laughed like a drain.

We could see the injured man up ahead of us, jammed in the angle of the steelwork beside the walkway. Stuck there he was safe enough, of course, but he was going to be a hard one to recover. When we reached him we found that he was lying on a steel meshwork plate to one side of the walkway. At least it gave us a surface to work on, even though looking directly over the injured man's shoulder there was a view of that unnerving two hundred feet or so of empty air.

It was not until that point I realised I should have brought a stretcher up with us. The patient was unconscious and unresponsive, and even if we were to revive him, the walk down that narrow walkway would be too much for him. Cesario, thank God, had a deck radio, holstered at his belt. He called for the stretcher while I examined the injured man.

As far as I could tell he had fallen from the upper part of the steelwork of the crane boom, a distance of perhaps fifteen feet or so. There was a bump on his head, a good deal of blood, and a mushy area at the back of his skull that felt as if it were damaged skin and flesh rather than pulped bone. This is always a delicate area of diagnosis offshore. There have been occasions when a medic, in all good faith, has missed a severe head injury, mistaking a skull fracture for a crushed patch of scalp, but this time, apart from the incredible amount of bleeding, everything seemed OK.

As I was leaning over him I dislodged a mouthgag from the open kit and it fell end for end, silvery in the lights towards the deck. Cesario roared with laughter. He said, 'That's it, English, throw things at the bloody deck crew, the lazy bastards deserve it. I tell you what. When we're finish up here we piss over them to teach them a lesson.'

The stretcher came up with two riggers, equally at home up here as their foreman. Lifting the patient was difficult because it was all to be done from one side but presently the casualty was strapped in and moved gently back down the crane towards the hospital. Cesario watched me as I went, unclipping the karabiners at each point.

'I never saw so many, many clips,' he remarked, but when we were finally down with the injured man on his way up to the hospital he added in parting, 'Hey, English. You should be a rigger. You got the balls for it. You want the job?'

In the hospital it was all so much easier. By the time he was in bed, and stripped, the man was already recovering and as there were no signs of brain injury I decided to hold him aboard until morning and then send him in for a check-up. In the meanwhile there was still the bleeding. A couple of stitches would close the cut but even so, the amount was ridiculous, and despite my best efforts it showed great reluctance to stop.

I said, 'Do you always bleed so much from cuts?'

It took a moment to sink in and then he said, 'No, señor. My brother he had a heart attack last year. He is only fifty-four and so I say to my doctor, how can I not do this thing too? And he said take aspirin. A tablet a day for ever, so I do.'

Aspirin, of course! All salicylates prolong clotting time and they are excellent at staving off heart attacks in high risk groups, but this was the most startlingly effective case I had ever seen. I closed the cut and left the man in the hospital, intending to check on him every half-hour or so.

Billy was still in the diving system control room.

'All right, Jon?' he said as I came in.

'Yes. No problem.'

'Good. High that crane, isn't it?'

'Damn right.'

'Yes. Well. Now you've had a go properly do you want the job permanently?'

'Yes. Yes, of course.'

'Right. You're on the team then. Good night.'

And with that we began a friendship and a working partnership that on and off lasted a full eight years.

4

After four weeks on *Hermod* we reached the end of the initial phase of the job and of our tour of duty. The Oseburg jacket was solidly secured to the seabed and topped off with navigational aids to warn off incoming shipping until we returned to put on the working deck some weeks later.

All diving jobs end with a series of speculations on where the next one will be. We always talk of who might be worth ringing. Names are bandied about, names who for most of us will always be no more than a voice on a long-distance telephone line. But these are the voices that send us to Aberdeen or Bergen or Tromso or further afield to West Africa or Singapore or Miri.

I decided to wait for Billy and the *Hermod*. He had already offered me a job on the second phase, and in any case I lacked the experience to play the field. Three weeks passed. I was by then certain that Billy had either forgotten his promise to use me again or had maybe never meant it seriously. The first paycheque, while satisfyingly large by onshore standards, could hardly last the winter. I began to consider phoning other companies. Finally the call came. Rejoin *Hermod* for phase two. Report Aberdeen 07.00 hours.

In the offshore industry, where a man is as good as his last job, a successful team can find itself in heavy demand while others, no less good but a little less lucky, languish onshore and wait.

Oseburg B was quickly followed by an inspection job in the British sector, then a recovery operation in November. By late summer I was finally feeling confident about the job.

* * *

It seemed that the long warm summer would never end. From famine the work situation rapidly reversed itself to glut. We spent all too brief periods on the beach between trips, but, by the end of September, I was established as a regular on Billy Carson's crew. I saw little of Gerry during that time. He had a team of his own to look after, but I heard from mutual friends that he was equally busy.

We were on the *Regalia* in the late summer. The year had presented nothing more fearsome to test my skills as medic than the incident on the big crane. The days were adding up nicely in my logbook and I looked forward to being fully qualified by the year's end; it seemed as if the investment would finally pay off. The *Regalia* was a very modern, extremely well equipped diving vessel, with truly luxurious accommodation that made her a favourite among North Sea crews.

It was on that job that a diver got religion in a big way. Now divers have many merits but religious belief is not one of them, by and large, so to meet a man like Tim Davis who constantly read the Bible, disapproved of swearing, and left the room if someone told a dirty joke, was an oddity in itself.

As always Billy was glorying in his reputation of a hard man who knew all there was to know about diving and had a reputation for not suffering fools at all. By then I knew how transparent that façade was, but it amused him and worried only new members of the crew. Even so, we were surprised at his choice of Tim to join the divers in saturation. Possibly his idea was to show a magnificent lack of bias.

The sat went quietly for the first week except that we noticed that on the night shift, when Tim was not diving and the main living chamber was mostly deserted, he would sit far into the night reading the Bible aloud in what should have been a deep, sonorous delivery, if the helium had not spoiled it rather.

Each night, whenever we checked the television monitor, there was Tim, reading his Bible. If the sound pick-up was on, the amplified and unscrambled voice would fill the control room pounding out the Book of Revelation. For a while it was amusing. Then slightly worrying and eventually, after twelve solid nights of this performance, it became a bore. We simply left the pick-up switched off, relying on the call buzzer for Tim to alert us if he actually wanted anything.

After two weeks he did. The buzzer sounded and I walked across to the unscrambler and selected the main chamber.

'Hello, Tim. What can we do for you?'

'I want to come out please, surface.'

'Pardon?'

'I need to be outside. God's work is not in here, in the chambers, but out in the world.'

George my shift supervisor was listening to this performance in disbelief. I felt exposed talking on the open link so I plugged in the headphones and mike set that allows private conversation with the chamber.

I said, 'Tim. Look, are you sure that you don't want to think about this?'

'No. You don't understand. God talked to me in the stillness of the night and I know what it is I have to do.'

'Look, Tim, I can't pull you just like that. You know that. It's not my decision.'

'That's all right. God will understand. Pass on the message in the morning.'

'Tim, are you sure that you couldn't wait twelve more days? After all, if God has managed without you for this long.'

'No. It must be soon.'

'OK, Tim. I'll pass it on.'

I took off the headset. George was looking at me questioningly.

'Well?' he said.

'He's got religion.'

'Well, he always had that. After all, he prays half the bloody night.'

'Yes, but he thinks God wants him out now.'

'Well, God will have to run the bloody decompression.'

'No, really man. He's really convinced.'

We looked at the monitor. Tim was carefully putting away his Bible and undressing. Just like any other night.

George said, 'He looks normal enough.'

'Yes. But for heaven's sake, he thinks he's got messages from on high. That's pretty well a ticket for the funny farm.'

'Do you think he's dangerous?'

'Who knows?'

He looked at me rather in the fashion of one who passes responsibility for a nasty job clean away.

'You're the medic.'

'Yes. But this is something else. I'll have to call the beach.'

Tim was peacefully tucked up in bed oblivious of our doubts as to his sanity.

Billy, when we finally told him, had no doubts.

'Right,' he said, 'get him the hell out as fast as possible. I want him isolated from the rest and I don't want him dived again. Do you have anything that will calm him down if we have to, Jon?'

'Yes,' I said, 'Largactil, if need be. But it's an injection, who's going to give it him?'

'You are. Who else?'

It was a very long decompression. For three days eleven hours and twenty minutes Tim was isolated in a chamber by himself, reading his Bible, eating his meals, sleeping regular hours, and in all respects acting as any normal citizen. All unaware that outside the door was the medical kit, and inside the kit was a ready use dose of the powerful sedative that would stop any aggressive moves on his part.

It was all unnecessary. He completed his decompression, stood his bendwatch (twenty-four hours the newly decompressed diver has to wait to make sure there are no delayed after-effects), and left for the shore without any sign of abnormality.

No sign of abnormality that is other than the fixed belief that God had spoken to him directly at 365 feet in a steel chamber in the middle of the North Sea. And who, I suppose, were we to argue he hadn't?

Later we heard that he had entered holy orders with one of the more evangelical churches.

*   *   *

It was on the same trip that we had a rush of medevacs. The 'medevac' system allowed us to ship an injured man home to hospital as fast as possible by using spare helicopter capacity from any aircraft in the area. I had never used it until about three days after Tim had gone I got a call to examine a deck-hand who had, so the story went, been walking along a hawser like a kid walking a curbstone when he fell off.

He was sitting on a lightweight plastic chair when I found him in the corridor outside the hospital. I could see right away that he was in a lot of pain. He was dead white and beaded with sweat, both classic shock symptoms, not usually associated with a minor fall. I moved him gingerly to the hospital and cut away first his boot and then the bright red overalls from the

left ankle. There was blood inside the overalls. Not a lot of
it but a broad crimson smear that sheeted down towards his
foot. I cut the cloth a little further, expecting to find a graze
or maybe a small cut and found instead a lumpy protrusion
on the outside of his calf. In the exact centre of this hump,
sticking through the skin, was a small splinter of dead-white
bone.

I had never before dealt with an open fracture but the drill was
clear enough. A ring pad of sterile gauze around the broken bone
end to keep the pressure off it, an ambulance dressing to keep the
bugs out and a call to the beach. Usually in circumstances like that
we get automatic permission for heavy pain relief. Once that meant
morphine sulphate, but thefts from hospital and lifeboat kits have
reduced our use of morphine and forced us back on substitutes like
Omnopon.

This time permission for pain relief was not forthcoming. We
strapped him to a stretcher in pain, shipped him to the helicopter
in pain and I assume still in pain after a ninety-minute trip, in pain
he arrived on the beach.

One case seemed to father another. The very next day, with
the weather rising, we were called out to a supply boat with
an injured man aboard. This time the condition of the casualty was less obvious, and more intricate. The man had suffered a sudden bout of renal colic which is extremely painful,
and once again I found myself refused pain relief permission
by the beach. He was not fit to fly alone and I went ashore
with him.

All the way in he was crying with the pain of the stone in his ureter,
all the way in I could do nothing but hold his hand and reassure him.
It seemed a long, long flight.

At Aberdeen Royal I talked to the admitting officer.

'Why did we not get permission for pain relief?'

'Well, morphine could mask symptoms.'

'OK and yesterday with an open fracture, what could we mask
then? And how about if we get a bad burn, do we let a man die of
shock?'

'No, of course not.'

'Look, either you trust us to do the job or you don't. If you don't
we might as well not be here.'

'In this case I felt morphine not to be appropriate.'

By now I was angry. I said, 'Look, it's a long way from home out there. We need your help not your bloody hindrance.'

'You can't talk to me like that.'

I looked around the hospital at the back-up facilities, at the signs to X-ray, at the dozens of nurses around. It was so safe, so secure after the rig. I said, 'So sue me. But I tell you this. If we have a big one, a really flat-out "shit-hits-the-fan" disaster, it won't be you in the front line.'

It was a remark that was to come back and haunt the both of us, but at the time it just felt like a stupid petty row over professional pride.

*   *   *

I had not seen Gerry all that season, but one mid-winter day, a day with a sky the colour of old lead, and the promise of snowfall in the air, he came to visit.

Our wives were both working and when the mood took him, he often used to come, attracted by the company and the log fire that burns through the winter in our living-room. Gerry has always carried a bit of weight but that day he was thinner, and there were bruised looking patches under his eyes. I sat in front of the fire saying little, but relaxed and taking in the warmth while the first ragged flakes of snow kissed off the windows.

'Well,' he said at length. 'Your first year. Do you like it?'

'Yes. It's better in some ways than I thought. Tougher in others.'

'How was the exam?'

I had sat the final licence exam just a week before, in an Aberdeen training room still festooned with decorations from Christmas.

'OK. Tough but fair.'

'Are things OK here?'

'Sure.'

'The thing is I need to ask you something. Has Judy said anything about Sue and me? I mean has Sue mentioned anything to her?'

'Sue? No, nothing.'

'Oh.'

'Are you having a bad patch?'

'Yes. Don't worry, mate, it will all pass.'

'If we can help?'

'It's all right. Forget I spoke. You want a drink?'

He reached into the pocket of his coat, where it hung over a chair back and took out a bottle of spirit so dark red it was almost black. Wood's Original Rum, over a hundred proof and rich with the perfume of molasses. He poured gingerly.

5

The early summer of 1988 was a slack time. In an industry that exists in a perpetual swing between boom and slump slack times are common, but during the summer we can usually count on a solid period of time offshore to carry us through the year.

It was because of that slack spell that I accepted the job on the *Ocean Victory* in the first place. It was outside my usual area of operations as Billy Carson's team medic, but Billy was himself on the beach and Gerry, whose dark premonitions about his marriage were temporarily in abeyance, was involved in a long-standing job in India. Both made sympathetic noises on the employment front and Gerry had half promised me a trip to Bombay but the *Victory* was a certain job and so I went.

She was old and tired and, like all drilling rigs, the accommodation was rough. Rigs are dirty too, and just about every surface that you touched came up with a thin, oily film of drilling mud.

To complicate things a bit more we were to support a drilling operation in the Piper field. This is an area that is known to be foul, with a great deal of hydrogen sulphide gas mixed in with the oil. Hydrogen sulphide is one of the real killer risks of the industry. In very low concentrations it is the familiar schoolboy stinkbomb smell of bad eggs, but high concentrations are more poisonous by far than cyanide and give no warning of their presence.

On foul wells there are a whole series of extra drills to go through to preserve some sensible degree of safety. Each man has to learn to use a Sabre rebreather set that will allow you to operate normally in lethal concentrations of gas long enough to reach a safe area. Sabre argue that it is impossible to seal a set with a beard and a great many long-cherished growths were shaved off on that job.

We were housed in a line of Portakabins on an outrigger over the water. Around thirty feet away was the flare boom used to burn off excess hydrocarbons if need be. As we went out to the cabins for the first time, someone suggested that at least it would be warm in the winter.

Victory was one of a series of similar rigs all of which had a certain reputation in the industry. One of her sister rigs had already been lost at sea off Newfoundland and a second sister, the *Ocean Odyssey*, was victim of a subsea explosion later that year.

She was not one of the Ocean Drilling and Exploration Company's finest, but it was a job when I needed one.

We went through the usual system checks on the chambers. Like the rig they were rather antiquated. They were also badly sited, perched on the lower deck right next to the central well that allows the drill string to pass from the drilling deck above to the sea. Parts of the system were hard to reach, and the control room was itself a Portakabin two decks away from the chambers. None of these things makes for easy running, but divers are usually an afterthought on drilling rigs.

From the cabin door we could see the platforms of the Piper and Claymore fields all around us. These were among the oldest in the North Sea, designed and commissioned during Tony Benn's 'white heat of technology' when the Arab oil embargo had made the race for production absolutely imperative. The nearest of them, *Piper Alpha*, was less than four miles to our east and it was on one of the wells we serviced.

The intention was to drill a deep slanting hole into the oil-bearing rock to allow the injection of water. This in turn would raise the pressure in the reservoir underneath and force the remaining oil to the surface. The problem was the gas pocket above the oil. We all knew very well what happens when a drill penetrates a hydrogen sulphide pocket. The last time it happened, in the Gulf of Mexico, the safety system should have worked perfectly. The annulus valve designed to prevent a rush of gas to the surface was, it was discovered later, in good condition. The gas they hit gave them no chance to activate it. No one can really know for sure, as the men who could have told the truth all died, but the theory is that enough gas came back up the well with the lubricating drilling mud from the bottom, to incapacitate the crew before they had time to react. Eighty-four men, the entire crew, were gassed to death.

The first job we had was to inspect the subsea structure. There was a well here already, feeding the *Piper Alpha* by a pipeline, and the driver had to turn a valve to isolate this pipe and recover some

equipment to the surface. At first the atmosphere of sitting on a
bomb got to everyone. But after a few days when nothing lethal
had transpired, we all began to relax into a routine.

There were, as it happened, a wide range of diving medics on the
Victory, plus a well experienced rig medic for the marine crew so we
all more or less reverted to our diving jobs. It was relaxing simply
to run a dive system and not have to hold a two-hour surgery at the
end of each twelve-hour shift. Being summer we had long soft nights
and balmy days with just a suggestion of morning mist to make the
sunrises more spectacular. Then, one night without a breath of wind,
the night of June 7th, it all changed.

We were in the control room playing cards and talking. There was
no diving that night and we had covered all the small jobs that needed
doing, though, according to contract, there were always a few divers
under pressure in the system, ready to dive at ten minutes' notice.
This was a raw team, new to each other and to the company, but
already by that stage we were confident of coping with the system
on the rig and, as the superintendent was asleep anyway, we were
relaxed.

Suddenly one of the deck crew came in.

He said, 'There's a fire on the *Alpha* platform.'

One of the others looked up from the cards.

'Bad?'

'I don't know. I had a look on the way here and it looked OK.'

My card playing is poor at any time, so I joined him and we
walked out on to a twilit deck to take a look. At that stage it
was idle curiosity. *Alpha* platform had all the usual technological
tricks to control fires. No one expected that this emergency could
be more serious than a practice launch of a few life capsules and a
quick burst from the firefighting semi-sub *Tharos* moored close to
the *Alpha* with a dive team of her own aboard.

Across the sea from us the platforms all looked normal. There
were flares in several places, and in the distance there was a confused
sound, as if bells and sirens might be ringing. But there was really
nothing to see. Then, part way up the boxy superstructure of the
Alpha platform, vivid against the dark of the steel work, a fire-rose
bloomed and licked upwards.

We both knew, standing there watching, that that flame was about
as bad as it could be. The *Alpha* was a production platform, a
gathering point for millions of gallons of oil and gas. She was

connected subsea to the main arteries that gathered oil and diverted
it towards the beach. Her fire suppression was designed to cope with
any possible eventuality, she had blast walls to contain explosions,
damping sprays that should extinguish burning gas, halon flood
systems to choke fires to death and yet she was burning.

The dive superintendent appeared from nowhere. He was a man
who had seen his own share of pain. He had battled cancer and won,
bossed teams around the world in an industry that does not promote
soft men and yet he looked tense and shaken.

'OK. You see the situation. We've no time to stand looking at it.
Get our rescue system ready in case. If the sea burns we'll have to
launch in a hurry. Also I need the oxygen unhitched as far as we
can and ready to ditch if need be. If the fire comes our way those
racks go over the side. Don't wait for the order to dump them. If it
looks difficult just do it. Come on lads, move, we've no time.'

A hyperbaric rescue launch is a theory exercise that none of us
expect to do in practice. It is a last-ditch operation, packing the
divers into a floating rescue chamber, maybe in a lifeboat, maybe
free floating, then abandoning them to the sea to float about, and
trusting to recover them before their gas runs out.

In *Victory* the second diving bell is the divers' lifeboat and we
cleared it for launch, climbing out over steelwork, checking valves,
opening gas bottles and rigging the big plastic floats that would keep
it on the surface.

When we were done the superintendent was back.

He said, 'I have to ask this. *Tharos* has requested that all available
medics go across to their hospital to help with any casualties. You
don't have to.'

Tharos is a class three firefighting ship. And by then she was close
up against the stricken platform, pumping water to cool what she
could. We had all trained a hundred times for this situation. Not
going was as impossible as flying to the stars.

'Of course we'll go.'

He looked at the three of us and shook his head.

'Good luck. You might need it. She's very close in to the fire.'

'How do we reach *Tharos*?'

'There's a Sea King in the area already. They'll pick up and take
you across. For now draw your survival suits and get to the hospital.
The rig medic will need help to pack extra gear.'

The hospital, a single room on the small rig, was all disruption.

Drugs cabinets, so tidy twenty minutes before, were ransacked for the essentials we expected to use. Plasma and morphine for burns. Space blankets for exposure cases. Needles and syringes to go with them. As we prepared, each of us was trying to come to terms with the unthinkable. We stuffed gear into cardboard boxes, lugged it to the helideck, sweating in bright yellow survival suits.

Outside the protection of the accommodation area the wind was breezing across the open space of the helideck, but it wasn't especially strong. For the North Sea it was nearly a flat calm. We waited on the companionway.

Up above we could hear the clatter of the incoming helicopter. It was not a civilian Sikorsky, no 'paraffin budgie' this; but a big international rescue yellow Sea King with Royal Navy markings. It filled the sky with noise and downdraft. Even out of direct line we felt the hot wind from the motors and smelled the burned Jet A, an evocative smell to all offshore oilmen, as it gets sucked into the ducts and wafted through the working spaces of the rig. It means the beginning of the trip. It means incoming mail, and, at the end of the trip, it means home.

The helicopter landing officer beckoned us up. The Sea King seemed huge, impossible that a great thing like that could set down on such a small deck. The side hatch was open and someone inside was pointing a TV news camera at us. He must have been quick off the mark when they got the call at Lossiemouth.

The supplies went in first, those cardboard boxes were going to mean life or death, we couldn't afford mistakes. They were quickly stowed. Then one by one, hauled in by the arms like children, dragging our suits over the lip of the hatch, we were lifted in.

It was no civilian aircraft. No plush orange seats and cosy briefing about flight times to Aberdeen. It had brown canvas slings and hefty webbing belts, and gear hanging in the gloom. Near the fire the flames lit up the cabin. Yellow suits looked a flickering orange, men's eyes caught the light and threw red highlights. There was a craning of necks to see out. Most of us only took one look. We were at perhaps seven hundred feet, circling in to land. Below us the *Tharos* was pumping a million gallons a minute from her fire monitors in great curving plumes of water.

Above us, impossibly high, towering over the helicopter like a malign God, the plume of thick, black, greasy, stinking smoke, shot even at that height with flames, burned.

Outside the helicopter on the deck of the *Tharos*, it was warm.
Not the soft warmth of a summer night, but a heat that was hard
and dry, so that you could feel your skin try to curl up in protesting
corkscrews. *Tharos* had a landing crew waiting for us. They grabbed
equipment as we passed it out. No one talked, no one smiled, they
were too pleased to see us to waste time on the formalities.

We hardly looked at the fire but we did take in what might matter
later. How wide were the steps? Could we get a stretcher up them?
Could we manage a spinal case through here? We thanked God for
good design. The steps were steep but broad enough to drive a taxi
up in comfort, only one difficult bend.

A crewman was waving us on. He said, 'Are you the medics?'

'Yes.'

'Hospital's this way.'

There was no time to think of training lessons now, it was all
frantic rush. Shucking yellow immersion suits in the corridor, we
just let them lie where they fell. The hospital had double doors
and with them shut the fire was closed out. The *Tharos* medic was
waiting to brief us.

'Right. The table there is for resuss. Drugs are over there.
Whatever you need take. Narcotics are in the small cabinet and
it's not locked, needles and syringes to the right. Burn dressings
are at the back. We'll use the cinema for the walking wounded.
Aberdeen is on full alert and a team of doctors will be here in a
couple of hours.'

We checked bed space quickly, instinctively each of us marking
up a territory to work in, then made a quick collection of supplies
we knew we'd need, dressing scissors, a space blanket, Roehampton
dressings for burns.

Someone called across the busy silence of preparation, 'Do we
have any Flamazine?'

'No.'

'Shit.'

Preparations went on. Time seemed to stretch for ever. We had
no casualties yet, and it seemed as if we'd been there for hours.
I checked my watch. It was twelve ten, only twenty minutes since
we'd left the *Victory*.

One of the deck crew came in dressed in overalls. In any other
hospital he'd have looked out of place but we had all come in
whatever we were wearing when the call-out came over the radio.

No one was wearing a white coat. No one had sterile clothing on. I found time to wash my hands in iodine scrub solution, as they were greasy from the Sea King's hatchway.

The others seemed so confident. For the first time we'd have no friendly casualty officer with thirty years' experience of mangled bodies to turn to as the court of last resort. That night we were all there was.

Reports kept coming in. Rescue vessel *Silver Pit* had picked up thirty casualties and many bodies. The gangway was across to the *Piper*. The gangway was on fire. The sea was burning around us. We knew that all this was simply talk, white noise to fill the vacuum of ignorance, but we still listened. No one went outside to find out. The discipline of training would have kept us in the hospital even if the place had really been on fire.

A crewman shoved the swing doors open with a bang. In his excitement he sounded like a TV film on Vietnam. 'We have landed multiple casualties. Where do you want them?'

The doors came open again and the first casualty was brought in. We all moved towards him in a rush. He was about forty with burns to his face, and maybe to the rest of him too. We lifted him on to a bed, dumping him in his dirty overall, on to white sheets.

Two of the others cut his clothes off. They smelled of seawater, of oil, of burning. He seemed not to realise what was happening, but he responded when I talked to him. His chest sounded rough. He had inhaled smoke and maybe some flame too. Later he'd need antibiotics to protect his lungs while they healed, if they healed. Later too, maybe medication to stop fluids waterlogging his lungs, but for now we needed an IV route for a drip and we needed oxygen and we needed both quickly.

I found the oxygen bottle by the side of the bed. It had a chrome key that had been cranked tight shut and for a few moments the thing wouldn't open. I had to go on my knees beside the bed to wrestle with it. Eventually it gave. Right away there was another problem. This man had facial burns. Wherever his body wasn't blackened by soot it was raw red where the skin had gone altogether. There was no way of strapping an oxygen mask to that destroyed face so I held it close to him, but not touching, so that he could breathe the gas.

More casualties came in. A small clutch of them backed up near the door. Some of the others moved into action while I held the mask. The man on the bed was trying to speak. His voice was soft and whispery like an old man with bronchitis.

He said, 'It doesn't hurt. That's good, isn't it? That it doesn't hurt?'

It wasn't good. It meant that he had full thickness burns. The nerves were burned away. But I said, 'Sure that's good,' and went on giving him the oxygen.

By then there were bodies on the beds, on the floor, and backed up in the corridor. I made sure that my first casualty was OK, got him to hold the mask in his good hand, checked the drip the others had put in, and moved on.

The next bed had an overweight guy with chest pains. Back in casualty they taught me that this sort of pain is often a heart problem but there they would have an ECG technician on tap. There was no way for us to be sure. He said he felt better sitting up. This is another classic warning of myocardial infarct. I mentioned it to one of the others. Between us we would watch him in case he suddenly deteriorated.

The log-jam of bodies was clearing now. The first rush of casualties was slowing down. Most of the beds were full and there were walking cases wrapped in blankets in the cinema next door. We were having problems getting an IV line into one of the burns cases. We had three different kinds of intravenous cannula from various rig hospitals, any one of them should give us a tube into a vein simply and more or less painlessly, but not one of them would work. His skin was charred black on both arms with folds of loose tissue hanging there and he needed the fluid. It was a problem that we faced again and again that night. Each of us felt for good skin with a reasonable blood vessel until finally someone slipped the bright steel needle into the blackened arm and the blood flowed wine red up the clear tubing so that we could start the drip.

I looked at my watch. Twelve thirty.

A crewman came in and asked for help on deck for a minute. I happened to be near the door so I went. Up on deck the heat was dry and hateful and made your skin crawl. Towering over us at the end of the barge was the fire, a column standing above us a thousand feet into the night sky. The metal of the structure was on fire and there were still men alive over there. Rescue boats ran close in to the burning platform, hauling men from the water. Occasionally you could see them in relief, a silhouette against a background of orange and red.

There were four bodies laid out on the deck. No one was prepared to shift them until someone had checked that they were really dead, though with such injuries there could really have been no doubt. I had seen men die before, but never so terribly. The deck-hand looked down at one of them. He reached out a hand to touch me. It was a tentative comforting gesture as old as humanity itself. But it was no sooner made than he seemed as if he were afraid that I might be offended at the contact.

'Are you all right?' he asked.

'Yes.'

'Poor bugger. Still it must have been quick.'

With those injuries it must indeed have been quick. I covered the ruined bodies as best I could.

'It's all right,' I said, 'they're all long gone.'

* * *

Already things were falling into order down in the hospital. Men were sitting up on beds talking to each other, grins born of relief split filthy, half-cooked faces, with teeth that looked very white.

Each man had a story to tell, each man needed to talk, to spill out some of the fear while it was still fresh, and the sheer relief of being alive would carry them through the horror. But we had no time to talk.

In the third bed there was a man with severe retrosternal pain. Something was wrong inside his chest and he kept drifting in and out of a muddy half consciousness. All of us knew that there were half a dozen possible causes, and we had no way of finding out for sure which of them we were dealing with. We had only the oldest diagnostic tools, common sense and basic instruments. No one wanted to make a decision on that case. The wrong move might kill him. We could not even give him pain killers because all we had were opiate based drugs, or their analogs, Omnopon, morphine sulphate, pethidine. All of them depress breathing and he had breathing problems already.

We worked on him in turn, each of the medics passing responsibility on. For the moment he seemed stable but this single case had already reduced us to shaman status. All at once all the training seemed a very thin defence in the face of such overwhelming disaster.

Finally he surfaced long enough to talk. He had jumped from the accommodation level. We reckoned he had fallen perhaps a hundred and fifty feet into the water, and he told us he had hit a deck rail on the way down.

With hindsight and this extra information we could see the significance of the bruise over the ribs on his right side. He hadn't taken much smoke but he may well have broken one or more ribs. We pressure bandaged the injured side, and his breathing and the pain improved immediately.

Just then my friend from the deck crew came back. This time a rescue team had taken casualties. On deck it was clear right away that things had gone badly wrong. The small high-speed semi-rigid launch had been caught in a ball of flame from an exploding riser. Apart from the heat, the fragments of steel from the ten-inch pipe had raked the area with shrapnel fragments. So far we had no way of estimating casualties.

They brought someone over the rails and they laid him very gently on the deck. An expectant ring of faces formed all around me. I felt for the rubber toggle of his suit zip and tugged it down. It jammed and I had to slice through the tough rubberised material with the dressing scissors. I tore the T-shirt underneath to reach his skin. He was so cold. Before I reached for the pulse in the hollow of the windpipe I already knew that he was dead.

I reached for the substernal notch, crossed my hands and pressed down. The rhythm was just like training, his ribs flexed easily. I stopped the heart compressions and moved to the head. Head back, I pulled a boot off the body to shove under his neck and keep the airway clear. I sealed my mouth round his lips. Blew. Twice. His chest rose and fell, rose and fell without the resistance of life. Then there was a rush of cold foul air, and the taste of salt water on his cheeks was suddenly thicker, more salt. I wiped the blood away from my mouth. The blast had killed him. Inside his chest the overpressure had shredded the delicate membranes of his lungs.

One of the other medics came up from below wearing a survival suit and carrying another for me. He looked down, felt the carotid pulse, shook his head. I reached into my pocket for the ophthalmoscope and looked into the dilated pupils of a dead man's eyes. There was no reaction to the light. In the maze of blood vessels on his retina there was no movement, instead air bubbles charted his mortality. 'Box Car Retina' the Americans call it. A crude ugly name for a tissue reaction that would be beautiful if it were not so final.

A voice broke through to me. 'Put the suit on. We're expecting the first evacuation helicopters within five minutes. They need one of us to each chopper and as many casualties as we can fit. Urgent cases first.'

I was still in the grip of that pointless paralysing reaction to the man's death. One death among so many. We all know about this kind of shock and he did the right thing. He threw the suit at me and knelt to talk through the din.

'He's fucking dead. There's nothing to do here. But they aren't. They need you too much for you to act like a bloody goosed fifth former. You've seen dead men before. You'll see them again before tonight's out. Get the fucking suit on.'

It was crude but it worked. I struggled into the suit. Shoes off first, legs in, pull the zips tight to force the air out of the leggings, central zip up, run a finger around the wrist seals to ease them off. The routine, familiar and mechanical, interposed itself to block the realities of that night.

We already had a small neat line of stretchers waiting to load when the first helicopter came in. They were the urgent cases. Casualties who the medics below had decided were hanging by a thread. The chopper came in fast. He circled the fire a couple of times and dropped neatly on to the deck.

He kept the rotors running, as the deck crew fixed the static earth line to the body of the aircraft and we started loading casualties. They had stripped some of the seats and we reckoned that we could get six, perhaps seven men, to a machine. The pilot and co-pilot watched the loading. We'd have liked to secure the stretchers properly but there really wasn't time and we had to rig them how we could.

We slung drips from luggage racks, from window releases, from seat backs. I was to go in with the first load. Take-off was rough, much faster than usual. Normally you go into a hover a couple of hundred feet over the sea while the pilot gets the balance of his machine before it goes nose down and flies off. This time I didn't feel the hover. We were off and away into the night before I realised it.

Away from the fire the night seemed full of navigation lights. There were choppers everywhere. Beacons flashed all around us. I gave a brief thought to air traffic control.

The lights in the cabin were dim, half yellow, and in the cockpit I could see a red lit instrument array. The co-pilot turned back towards me and beckoned me forward. He had to shout to make himself heard as I was not on intercom net.

'Seventy minutes or so to Forester Hill. We'll go direct to the hospital. Will they all make it?'

'Ask me when we get there.'

I went back into the cramped half-lit chaos of the cabin and the machine clattered on into the busy air space.

One of the drip bags was very close to empty and I pulled the adaptor out of it and held the open end of the line low, pinching the tube to keep air bubbles out of the liquid. The new one punctured easily and I adjusted the flow. Precision wasn't really important or possible at that stage. It was just habit. I checked around the cabin. Most of the men were resting as if asleep. One or two were watching me. The co-pilot glanced back and I gave him the thumbs up.

Just then something made me check the pulse of the guy with the drip. He didn't look so very different but in those few seconds his heart had stopped. I felt for the carotid pulse. Sometimes you can feel pulses there when the wrist has failed. I felt supple flesh, warm and slightly bruised with beard growth, but no pulse.

I'd never done CPR in anger before that night but by then it was a familiar routine. I gave him three or four quick inflations then thumped his chest hard. It's a method pioneered by the Americans called precordial thump; the idea is to give the heart a quick shove into action.

The pulse returned instantly, slow and uncertain but it was there. He would live. At least this time. I sat on the deck of the aircraft and held his wrist lightly, counting the beats. It was steady, weak and thready, but steady. I found it hard to leave him to check the others. Having survived this near miss I felt close to him and felt that he had first call on my attention, but at Aberdeen they'd need the best information I could give them on all the patients in the load.

One of the men needed to urinate. We should have thought of this before the flight but there was no time. Logic told him to wet himself but conditioning was too strong. Finally I found an empty polythene sheathing from a drip bag. He used it gratefully.

In burns cases urine output often becomes a problem. All too frequently the bladder fills and the victim is unable to relax and pass water. So far we had avoided this but that was more luck than anything else. We do carry Foley catheters but the thought of passing the fifteen inches of latex into the urethra of

a man already so injured as most of these seemed torture added
to injury.

Our approach to Aberdeen was different from the usual flight
path. Usually we hug the coast, running in over marshes and dunes
for half an hour. Incoming, it is good to watch that coastline. It
prolongs the pleasure of arrival and heightens the anticipation at
the end of twenty-eight days at sea, but all I wanted to see right
then were the lights of the city.

Aberdeen came up below us. Streets beaded with lights, cars
crawling along and ahead a patch of flickering blue beacons in front
of the hospital. I know Forester Hill. I've medevaced more than a
few men to the place and it's normally got the busy efficiency of all
big hospitals about it. That night it seemed chaotic. The helicopter
came in to the circle a hundred yards or so from Accident and
Emergency. I expected the police of course and the fire brigade,
that's standard for an emergency landing, but there were far more
TV and press crews than I had expected.

From the beginning of the emergency we had been effectively
isolated. Radio communications from site were cut, except for vital
messages. We knew nothing of the TV news flashes that had alerted
half the world to the plight of the stricken platform.

As soon as the aircraft landed the door opened and we started to
discharge casualties. At this point the order that we took them in
was vital. I went in with the arrest patient, running down a corridor
of newsmen and their lights, holding a drip in one hand and the
stretcher with the other.

The triage officer was at the door. I said, 'This one arrested on
the way in. He's had two, maybe three, units of plasma and he's
got forty per cent full thickness burns. Maybe taken some smoke
as well.' Details of the drugs given were pinned to his chest. They
rushed him away into the hospital. Other patients followed to be
sorted in quick succession. Doctors moved in to cubicles. I felt flat
and redundant.

A sister came over to me.

'This man in cubicle six. Do we have his name?'

'Not unless it's on the paper that's pinned to him.'

'And has he been given any drugs?'

I went to look at him. He was an impact case, the one with chest
pains. I said, 'Nothing apart from fluid.'

'How much fluid?'

'One I know of.'

'You're not sure?'

She sounded shocked. I wanted to tell her that in the first rush we had had no time to count and classify.

I said, 'Things were a little rushed.'

'All right.'

There was sympathy in that voice. Maybe she did understand.

She asked, 'Would you like a coffee?'

'I've to go back with the aircraft.'

'No. They've already left. You're going back with the next one.'

I moved into the reception area. There was a glass screen with a big office and phones. All of them were ringing but no one answered. A kid with a cut hand was sitting waiting for examination. Her blood dripped slowly, her face was streaked with tears.

I was still wearing a survival suit and it marked me out. A reporter came up to me. He was very young and fresh looking. He said, 'Can I have a few words?'

'You'd be better asking the information officer.'

'You were there. He wasn't.'

'OK.'

'How many casualties do you think that there are?'

'God knows.'

'You've no idea?'

'None.'

'OK. Fine. You were working in the hospital?'

'Yes.'

'And you are a . . . ?'

'Medic. Dive team medic.'

'Were there any doctors out there when you left?'

'No. They were on their way.'

'Would you say there was a good deal of panic?'

I didn't like that question. Sure he had a right to know but it smacked of tabloid trivialisation and I said, 'The platform burned under them. What do you think?'

'Were the facilities enough?'

'Yes.'

'You wouldn't mind if we interviewed you on camera?'

I had a vision of this on national TV.

'Not before I ring home.'

'I'm sure they'll all be proud of you.'

'Not before I ring home.'

He smiled his safe supercilious smile.

'We could ask one of the other people,' he said, with the air of a man making a silky threat.

'Sure, you do that, and you know what else? If you don't show a bit more humanity when you interview them you might be needing treatment yourself.'

He recoiled a bit. Still he only looked about nineteen. Just a kid trying to build a name for himself. He backed off anyhow and went to bother someone else. A woman had been watching us through all this. She was mousy red-haired, small, youngish. She waited like a schoolkid trying to break into a conversation between adults while I punched buttons on the coffee machine. I thought she was perhaps another reporter but she said, 'My husband. He was on the *Piper*. Have you seen him?'

She gave me a name. It didn't ring any bells then, though I have never forgotten it since.

She said, 'He was on the night shift maintenance crew.'

'Well a lot of the night shift made it. But things are a bit hectic out there now. Look, don't read too much into my not having seen him. He's probably all right.'

I knew it was a lie really. The odds were not good, but I could not look into that ordinary face and tell her he was probably dead.

We heard another helicopter incoming and I swilled the rest of the coffee. She was still standing there looking at me. I said, 'I'm going back out there now, I'll look for him, I really will.'

'Tell him if you see him that Julie's waiting at the hospital. Will you do that?'

There was desperation in that voice. I could tell she knew the odds well enough. But I promised just the same.

Outside, the press were gathered in numbers. It was hard to get through to the machine, and two or three times we had to shove them out of the way. Finally I made it to the helicopter steps.

One of the other medics was there.

'Jesus, what a circus.'

'Bloody press.'

'There's a crew on the *Tharos*.'

'What? Who let them in?'

'The Navy. They were filming on the Sea King when they got the call-out.'

We sat in the seats of an empty helicopter, saying nothing, thinking as we flew back out to sea.

* * *

There were a lot of aircraft stacked in the area of the platform waiting to go in with supplies and to pick up casualties. We circled out of range of the turbulence above the fire. By that point there was a cordon of exclusion around the site to keep the press and spectator boats clear of the operation, and a stacking system was operating for incoming helicopters.

From up there the fire seemed reduced in scale, but, as we moved closer to take our turn at landing, we could see that the whole structure below the helideck level was engulfed in flame. It seemed impossible that anyone could still be alive in that cauldron but they were. On the last open space of the helideck, surrounded by a sea of fire, dark in orange survival suits against the gold and red of the flames' reflection, there were still men.

There was no logic to them being there. No one could have set an aircraft down in that fire even if a crew could be found who were willing to try. The heat must have been intense so close to the flames, and the updraft would have made landing impossible in any case. I wanted to look away from these men who were already dead, even while they still lived. But that felt like one final betrayal inflicted on men who were already betrayed. We could not reach them, we couldn't even offer a word of comfort, we could only watch so they did not die entirely alone.

As we continued our circuit of the wreck I hoped each time that there would be an ending for them. Smoke poisoning or lack of oxygen, anything to spare them, and us, the agony of their watching us for the help that we could not give.

The *Tharos* was spraying the wreck with water and the men on the giant fire monitors were trying to help as best they could by cooling the deck around the men who were trapped down there, gathered in a group in the centre of the open deck space, as far as they could get from the flames. Surely the fire must starve their air supply soon, but still they stood and waited for the rescue that we were powerless to offer them. The *Tharos*'s fire monitors were the best in the world, monsters that could drive the whole vessel backwards with the force of their recoil, but they were still not enough.

The blast of air when it came was enough at 500 feet range to rock the helicopter sideways. There was a multicoloured ball of flame,

yellow and white and red. It rose past us, mushrooming into the
night sky, and for a second we could see the outline of a second
aircraft, below us in the stack, dark against the flames.

When the fireball cleared, the helideck and the survivors were
gone. The steelwork where they had stood was twisted in the heat,
and still, implacable, as if it could never have enough death to
glut itself, the fire burned on. It was the darkest point of the
long night.

As we came in to land on the helideck no one said very much.
There didn't seem much to say any more. We passed a second
crew taking off outgoing injured. We got time for a few seconds'
handover.

'Are the medical team here yet?' I asked.

'No, but we heard that they've left Aberdeen.'

'Great.'

'How is it there?'

'The press are a bloody pest. There are cameras everywhere.
Look, if you get a chance to ring home could you ring in for me?'

'Of course.'

I gave him a number but we knew that the lines out from the
hospital were going to be blocked for hours.

We waited on the deck for a few minutes, helping out with
outgoing injuries. These guys didn't look so bad. They were men
from the first flush of casualties. Most of them minor, walking
wounded. I came across one man sitting alone and asked him how
he was. He didn't respond and at first I thought that he must have
been in shock but then I realised that he was deaf. From the blast
probably. We smiled and touched like a couple of lunatics, each
trying to reassure the other. I think he was simply glad to be alive.

We made sure that each man was wrapped in a blanket, each man
marked with medication details. Even in such a short time responses
had improved. We were more professional, more efficient, less
involved.

The fire was roaring away a few hundred feet in front of us. At
least we didn't need to trouble about the chilling effect of the night
air. If it weren't for the fire it would still have been dark. The sea
looked oily smooth, flat calm, reflecting the flames.

There was a commotion on the deck. Someone had spotted
a man climbing the remains of the steelwork. Looking closely,
squinting against the light and heat of the fire, we all saw him.

A black shape climbing the spidery steel with the flames rising all around him.

One of the fire monitors shifted ponderously, the great plume of water slewed so that it fell on him in a cooling shower. They couldn't turn the water on him directly or the force of the jet would knock him off the steel into the flames. Mentally, we were all right there with him climbing, each man on the deck was willing him to somehow escape. Then the steel fell. It went over sideways like a giant kneeling and collapsed into the sea.

We didn't see the man fall but we all felt it. Down there where he had struck the water the sea was burning from the oil spill.

As I went back into the hospital one of the other medics stopped me and looked at my arm.

'OK, over there,' he said. 'I'll get to you as soon as I can.'

'What? I'm a medic, not a bloody casualty.'

'You're bleeding.'

I'd felt nothing but there was a bloody rip in my survival suit. Something had travelled past me fast enough to slice a clean nick into my forearm. One of the others doused it with peroxide, stuck a plaster on it and swabbed the blood with a lump of cotton wool.

Another casualty was carried in and I started in on him. Under his clothes he was dead white and crinkled. He had been in the water a long time before the rescue craft found him. Also he was not shivering, which is not a good sign.

I tried to turn him on to one side but he was heavy and I asked a deck-hand who had come in search of a stretcher to help. There was no point in taking this patient's temperature at the body surface. I could feel that he was cold without that. It's the body core that counts here. Below 32 degrees Celsius he would be in serious trouble, below 30 and we might not be able to revive him.

I spread his buttocks for the rectal probe and slipped the thermometer in. We waited, the deck-hand holding one side while I took the weight on the other. The patient seemed dead but for a slow pulse and a shallow fluttering breath every now and then. There were no burns and no bruising.

After three minutes I checked the temperature – 30.6. Not good but not impossible. We rolled him into the coma position so that if he should vomit he wouldn't choke. I reached for a space blanket. They come in a small packet of polythene about seven inches by four, and they always look inadequate.

Opened out the aluminised foil would retain most of his body heat. We don't use aggressive rewarming, like dumping the patient in a bath of hot water. If his skin was warmed too fast the remains of his body core heat would flush to the warm skin and he might die.

He lay there breathing shallowly, eyes closed, as white as death. I made out the note for him. Scribbled it on a torn-out sheet of A4: 'Injuries unknown. Unconscious and unresponsive on arrival. Body temp 30.6 rectal. No drugs. No pain relief. Probably simple Hypothermia.'

Someone arrived with a couple of cases of Coke and a big box of Mars Bars. As we passed by we helped ourselves. We needed the energy. It was two hours and thirty minutes into the emergency.

* * *

There was a blast sufficiently extreme to rock the whole vessel. We clutched on to whatever was handy, trolleys, beds, stretchers, while the turbulence passed. Up till then no one had really given a great deal of thought as to the risks of simply being there. *Tharos* seemed big, safe and competent in the face of the fire. Suddenly she seemed vulnerable.

Fresh injuries came through the doors in a steady flow. We had casualties lying in the corridor now, and in a small side ward, quiet in the friendly gentle darkness that they could no longer appreciate, we had the dead.

A man was brought through the queue for immediate treatment. One look and I could see why they had rushed him through. Something had torn a great gaping wound in his scalp. A flap of skin, flesh and hair was displaced to one side giving him an odd cockeyed look as if he were wearing a cap at a jaunty angle. I ran quickly through the neuro exam, talking to him, all the time gauging awareness of place, time, orientation; holding a great wodge of gauze to the head wound meanwhile. He looked far worse than he was. The scalp wound would stitch, layer by layer, to leave, in the end, a fine puckered white line under his hair.

On a normal night on a rig in quiet times I would close this wound, but now he must be medevaced with the rest. I rested my hands on his scalp and eased the displaced tissue into something resembling normality, clipping it to contain the worst of the bleeding, and wrapping a sterile dressing over the wound. He seemed oddly cheerful. Maybe he had expected to die. On the other hand maybe he was going into shock, maybe his brain was bleeding under that sickly white bone that I was looking at a few seconds before. There were a thousand maybes and no answers, no certainties. There was only the crude uncertain care that we could give, and as the night went on it seemed more and more inadequate.

I scribbled out the notes: 'Scalp wound. No concussion, neuro/obs initially normal. Re-examine every half-hour.'

As I wrote it I knew that there was no chance of that. Maybe if he fell off his chair in a heap we might get to re-examine him, otherwise there were too many competing needs. I took him through to the cinema, sat him in a plastic chair, wrapped a cellular blanket around him.

There were fresh burn cases coming in. These were perhaps the worst injuries of the night. The triage medic looked drawn and white. His was the very worst responsibility of all. He must decide life and death. No one blamed him for letting them all through.

We were short of large Roehampton dressings. Short of plasma expanders, short of dextrose in saline. We waited for the emergency team from Aberdeen, we needed the drugs that they had almost as much as we needed their expertise.

We worked in pairs, slitting waterlogged overalls from burned bodies, assessing severity and depth of burn. We gave controlled drugs where we had to now. Countersignatures, the law, the register of use, were all suspended in the face of need.

A man lay burned from head to foot, blackened, smelling of the fire. Only his eyes were still alive and aware in that cruelly abused face. I could not offer him the comfort of touch; where the skin was not completely destroyed it would have been agony, and besides, I was afraid that my hands would convey bacteria into the burned, sterile tissue. We gave him oxygen but his breathing wasn't too bad. I could not take his blood pressure. There was no way that I could strap a pneumo cuff on to that charred limb, but it was clear he needed fluids.

Normally putting in a drip is a quick job. Most of the men we deal with are young and, before injury hits them, in the prime of life. Their veins are most often like fire hoses. Not that time. I put on a pair of Kimguards, the slick stretchy plastic encased my hands. Even the French chalk inside them didn't dry up the sweat on my palms.

I tried to visualise the vein without touching him. It was no good, his forearm was an alien landscape. I looked at his legs. We don't often use leg veins for drips because it increases all the risks, but I'd have used anywhere with a clean area of skin.

Nothing. Blackened, oozing red, cratered like the rest of him. I touched his forearm in the crook of his elbow. The burned skin felt odd like thin tanned leather through the gloves. I thought I felt a warm spot, and pressed it gently. He moaned but I had to keep the pressure on for a moment to be sure. Then I felt a pulse. No good. That was an artery. I had hoped to get by without a pressure cuff but there was no choice, there never really was a choice. I wrapped the Velcro band around his upper arm and pulled it as tight as I dared. A little bead of blood, bright ruby red, formed below it. He said nothing but I could feel the hurting coming off him in waves.

I almost wanted him to cry out. I found his heroism in the face of my kindhearted cruelty unbearable.

The skin peeled under my touch, and then swelling the raw red surface I felt the vein. My partner, who had stood beside me saying nothing, understanding everything, passed me a cannula kit.

Usually we use the butterfly needle with a simple plastic fitting to join it to the giving set, but we had only Medicuts left. They look like a small hypodermic syringe with a three-inch long, wide bore needle on the end. The sharp point penetrated his raw flesh easily, cleanly. I felt the pop of the vein and aspirated with the syringe. Deep red blood flowed back. I rested the syringe on the bed for a moment to reach for the free end of the giving set tube.

At that precise moment his resolve broke. He groaned, tried to sit up, and the syringe, the cannula and his blood fell to the deck. We had to do it all again.

The second time was harder.

In the next bed two others were putting in a catheter for a man who could not pass urine. When they reached it, it was cloudy. We didn't have a clear history on him either. It could have been anything from the effect of the burns to the onset of crush injury syndrome. We could only medevac and hope.

I went up to the deck with the next load for the beach and climbed into the helicopter that brought the medical team. Eight casualties this time, lying where we could strap them across the seats of the Super Puma. Most with burns, most with drips. All with notes pinned to them. I had three bags of Gelofusine plasma expander with me, all that we could spare.

This trip was easier. I even had time to talk to the pilot and co-pilot on the way in, and no one died. The fire was less awe-inspiring now. Most of what would burn had done so.

Aberdeen Royal stretched out in front of us. There was a full fire crew by the helicopter pad, flashing blue beacons patterned the night, and from our height, away in the east the first pink fingering of the dawn was rising.

I went through the ritual of discharge. Notes, explanations, handovers. One of my injured was the deaf man from earlier. He grinned and shook my hand before casualty swallowed him up.

I sat in a quiet spot in the treatment area. I could almost have fallen asleep. Then there was someone beside me. The same ordinary face, the same crack-brained hope. I shook my head.

'Sorry, love. I've not seen him yet.'

'But he might be on another boat?'

'Yes.' (No chance.) 'He might.'

'Those suits they give you.' She touched the sleeve of it like a talisman. 'They keep you alive in the water?'

'Of course they do. You can stay in the water for hours wearing one.'

But if you did, you'd be dead. This wasn't the training pool in Aberdeen. This was the North Sea and besides it wasn't cold that we were worrying about.

'You think he'll be OK?'

'Sure he will.'

I moved back into the treatment area. There I was tolerated, treated with kindness, like a country cousin come to visit. There I was not asked to play God and to say that her man had survived, when he was among the dead.

* * *

Back aboard *Tharos* the medical team from Aberdeen had left great stacks of neat aluminium cases just inside the hospital door. They were mainly open, spilling drugs and syringes, plastic bags of plasma expanders and giving sets in their blister packs, on to the deck.

I felt less needed now that the doctors were there, but we quickly realised that they too were overwhelmed by the scale of the disaster. They had practised for this eventuality again and again but no one really anticipated the realities of the situation.

There was a fresh flush of casualties. I went up on deck into the blood-red light of the fire still wearing a survival suit which very quickly became too hot. Dumping it on the deck, I was given instead a bright green body-warmer with MEDIC across the back in huge letters. I felt ridiculous.

Silver Pit, a converted trawler acting as rescue and standby boat, was alongside. Floodlights picked out the mechanical details of her decks. Winches, cables, quads of compressed gas – and casualties.

There were fewer than in the first flush. Most by now were either saved or dead. They were passed across to us with the best rough gentleness that we could muster.

One man was lying still. He was peaceful, unmarked, with no sign of violence on his face, a red blanket drawn up to his chin, his eyes closed as if in sleep. He still wore the orange overalls that he must have put on clean to go on shift. I felt his wrist. Nothing, cold waxy emptiness, no flicker of life. Maybe the carotid pulse. I felt the gristly rings of his windpipe, slipped two fingertips into the hollow on one side, still nothing. I tore open his shirt to expose his chest as one of the deck-hands came over.

'Don't bother, mate. He was dead when we landed him and that was two hours since.'

'OK.'

He shook his head and said, 'I'm sorry. He should have gone to the morgue.'

'Not your fault.'

I touched the cold wet hand and squeezed the fingers. Yes, I could feel the beginning of rigor. The deck-hand was looking at me uncertainly.

'It's all right,' I said. 'Like you said, he's been dead hours.'

A casualty sat beside me on the open deck. He was not badly hurt but no one was paying him much attention and so he sat on a bollard and cried. The tears were like gold in the light of the fire and they dripped steadily on to his nose and fell to the bulge of his knees. He kept saying 'Christ, all my mates,' again and again.

I took him down to the hospital where one of the doctors okayed me giving him a Valium. He looked very young and very scared and very much out of his depth. Nothing had prepared anyone for this.

I rooted through packages of drugs and found a jar of green and black capsules. Librium. Not quite what I was looking for but near enough. I palmed a couple and gave them to my casualty with a glass of water. His swallowing was mechanical. I could have given him poison and he would have taken it. I gave him a quick check-over. No bruising, no external damage, no neurological warning signs. He was physically OK, but mentally he wasn't there any longer. I left him sitting on a bed and when I looked again five minutes later he was still in that same position. Sitting with his thumb straying towards his mouth, slack jawed, dull-eyed; far away from the realities of the present.

A group of doctors surrounded a naked, badly burned man on the resuss couch. One of them was sounding his chest. The casualty was burned black over most of his body, but how much was soot and how much damaged tissue was hard to say. He was moaning in a high-pitched voice that hurt you to listen to. No one had a right to resent that, but the sound frayed nerves.

I filled a syringe with morphine for one of the doctors. While he held the patient at an angle so that he could inject into a region of intact thigh, I was about to swap needles when he stopped me.

'No time for that. Just get rid of the air and give it me.'

The needle sank deep into the muscle and it quivered at the fresh assault. There were a few moments of calm and I could hear the faint hiss of the syringe sucking air. Presently the patient relaxed, became tractable and dreamy, stopped hurting. He was booked for the next medevac.

It was five in the morning and the flow of injured men had slowed to a trickle. There was very little hope for those left in the water now, but outside the rescue vessels were carrying out a perfect geometric search pattern. They were doing it by the book, following the set of the tide and leaving not one single square foot of water untouched.

The hospital had lost its air of battlefield dressing station. We still had one injured man who needed constant observation but there were doctors enough and to spare, so I went out on to the deck.

The dawn was well into the sky, lighting a perfectly calm, deceptively innocent North Sea. Of *Piper Alpha* platform there was left only a single tower, a flare boom, and a fragment of burned and rusted superstructure, looking already a hundred years abandoned to the ocean. Nearby, oil still burned at the surface of the broken subsea risers, the flames rocking gently in the swell.

We were asked, maybe because we were available and medics, to help to enclose the dead in the black heavy plastic body bags. Going down to the bare steel room that was our temporary morgue, I had expected to be an ordeal to end all the others. In fact, although there was more than enough of purely visual horror, the silence and the final peace of those mute corpses, who had fought the battle of the elements and lost, softened the pain of the night.

We straightened each of them as far as burns and circumstances permitted, and closed the heavy-duty zips over silent faces.

Outside, when we got back on deck, the medical team were collecting their aluminium cases ready to go home to Aberdeen. There was an air of a job done, if not well, then as well as it could have been done. They shook each of us by the hand as they left. The circumstances changed the small formality almost to a ritual.

As we were walking back towards the galley for a hot drink, a stretcher landed from a rescue craft. We moved towards it, ready for whatever new trial this one would bring, but the deck-hand carrying the front end shook his head.

'It's all right, lads. He won't be coming in.'

It was the last corpse that we landed that night.

*   *   *

We stood waiting in our yellow and black suits for a shuttle from the *Tharos* back to our own vessel. A few hundred feet away the risers still burned. It was the image that would dominate the press coverage of the disaster. A black plume of smoke rising straight into a blue summer sky and that scarred and battered wreck.

Back on the *Victory* we all wanted to call home. In theory the company should have done this already but we needed to make the contact ourselves. The line was dreadful. The satellite was blocked by essential traffic, so we had instead to go through the shoreside radio service. Through the static we each in turn called our wives, reassured them that we were alive and safe, passed on our love across the empty space.

Going home, three days after the event, the sound and fury was almost finished. Aberdeen Heliport was quiet as always and the only traffic was oil related. Wives met husbands and hugged them close, greeting them home from the sea. The few scattered pressmen were bored now. The story was no longer hot at that point. Instead there were the recriminations and the endless theories produced by shore-based experts who put forward complex and beautifully structured theories, and talked of them endlessly in earnest late-night TV programmes, as if any of that really mattered any more.

Three of us were travelling back on the afternoon train out of Aberdeen to the South. We gathered in the station bar at a tall round table with ridiculous stools that needed a small jump to climb into them. The train rattled south, past the oil company bases beside the railway line, and out into the flattish countryside along the coast.

Beside us, in the bar, a drunken rigger was holding forth to anyone who would listen. No one gave him even a flicker of attention but that didn't put him off at all.

He said, as far as you could understand through his accent and the drink, 'I'll fucking never go back there, you know. That was fucking it. I can live with the weather and the muck and the hours, but when they fucking start killing people.'

He glanced across at us.

'Were you not on the *Tharos*?' he said.

I said, 'No, not us, mate. You must be thinking of someone else.'

He swayed a little.

'Well, I'll not be going back. Fuck the bastards. I'll never go out there again.' Then he paused to take a pull at his drink and he seemed almost sober for a moment as he said, 'Unless I have to, like.'

* * *

For months after that night on the *Tharos* we heard stories of men who were haunted by their memories or even wracked by an irrational guilt that they were among the survivors while so many others were dead. For myself and the rest of our medical team, I know of no one who would willingly have traded places to be elsewhere that night.

I was in fact quite ready to go back to the North Sea but, as things turned out, Gerry fetched up on my doorstep one morning some three weeks after the *Alpha* disaster and his offer was very different indeed.

'India,' he said. 'Bombay High. You'll like it. Honestly.'

'Is there anything special I should know about this trip?'

'Just make sure that your tropical vaccinations are up to date.'

6

Bombay greeted us with a thousand smells and a hundred per cent humidity that had us sweating even before the airport bus disgorged us into the marble transit halls of Sahar International.

Gerry was relaxed on home ground, but for me that first sight of India will always be a moment of real magic that stands out in a decade's travelling.

India is the most brightly coloured country I have ever seen. And it is a crowd, a vast travelling population, a massive transient herd that moves from city to city, from state to state, visiting relatives, selling goods, spreading sedition. In India it all seems to be one. It took us an hour to clear customs, another forty minutes to clear Immigration, and all the time the vast endless cavalcade never slacked a fraction.

We took an autorickshaw to the hotel, the yellow and black three-wheelers that are so dangerous that they are banned completely from the inner parts of the city. At every traffic light beggars held out emaciated hands for coins. The night was full of scents and bright lights. Joss fought with the smell of excrement. Cows wandered in the suburbs and small herds of bleating goats scattered as we roared through bright lit back streets.

After the cavalcade of our arrival, the Centaur Hotel, government run, five star, and air-conditioned to an icy cool, was a culture shock of its own, with a lobby the size of an aircraft hangar. It was all white marble and, lit with clusters of small clear glass, it looked like a fairytale castle built for an Eastern Disneyland.

'If you think the city is fun,' Gerry said as we were ushered to our rooms by a huge man in Pathan costume, 'wait till you see the ship.'

To join the ship we had to drive the whole length of Bombay harbour, a distance of fifty miles or so, passing the imposing bulk of the Gateway to India where so many fresh young servants of the

British empire arrived a hundred years ago, though, significantly, the building is now a public urinal. The road to the oil base at Nhava was a constant stream of trundling autorickshaws, decrepit Maruti taxis, and pedestrians. At each traffic light our bus was surrounded by beggars, exhibiting crude amputations, running sores, eyes milky with cataracts.

We were nearly in Nhava when we saw the beggar on a skateboard for the first time. He was a man of indeterminate age, brown cheeks stubbled with white, eyes red rimmed, and he was legless. The stumps were roughly bound in bandages and he rode on a bright green skateboard. What set him apart from the mass of others was the two-foot length of wood that was penetrating the muscles of his chest so that it protruded from both sides. It looked like the aftermath of some freakish industrial accident, but the man seemed healthy enough, and as the traffic moved off, he grasped the rusting steel bumper of a water bowser and was hauled, in a cloud of foul blue exhaust, to the next intersection.

Even the most callous of the crew was appalled by the sight of this legless, mutilated body. But at that point the bus turned out of the traffic and on to a red dust track guarded by a uniformed man hoisting an ancient Enfield .303. Above him there was a bright lettered sign. 'ONGC NHAVA' it said. We had arrived.

Nhava is a classic oil base. That is, a port sited as far away as humanly possible from the temptations of the town.

India's strict land distribution laws being what they are, the original village of Nhava on which the oil base dumped itself could not be moved, so, drawn by the prospect of foreign money and rich pickings, it made the best of things and now has electricity and two bars, one of which proudly sports the hand-lettered sign that proclaims it 'The Nhava Hilton'. We checked in aboard the *Sevak* and it was late in the afternoon by the time we found ourselves in the bar's single room with the few tables and wooden benches, lit by a naked bulb that drew its power direct from the dockyard supply via a system of bare wires that gave anyone unwary enough to touch them a highly unpleasant jolt. There was a large beer cooler, several lizards, a dog and a goat.

The goat itself has achieved a degree of fame among the oil workers who pass through the place, because, late at night when the rest of the village are in bed, and the only people up are the oilmen and the bartender, the goat lies on a charpoy outside the bar window and grins. Indeed the 'Grinning Goat of Nhava' has achieved fame throughout Bombay High Field.

In the humidity of the late evening we drank Kingfisher beers that became lukewarm almost as soon as they poured from the bottle into the glasses. We talked of the vessel which was excellent, modern and well found, of the climate which was dreadful, and of India. Presently the beggar on the skateboard arrived. His agility in manoeuvring the thing down a track that was at best roughly graded was remarkable. He rolled into the tiny cramped bar holding out a bowl and crying 'Halah' again and again in a flat voice. The barkeeper made to throw him out but the party had been going on for some hours by then and it was already fairly mellow, so, inevitably, someone bought the old man a beer, and there he sat on his skateboard, which was adorned with a stick-on decal of Bart Simpson, and drank his drink.

The wooden stave protruded through the cloth of his ripped and filthy shirt. The wounds, where it penetrated the skin, however, looked fairly clean. The old man sat and drank and presently someone produced a bottle of Old Monk rum and he got well into that as well. At about that point Dave suggested that we could do something more practical to help the old beggar.

Dave was a tough-minded, pragmatic sort of man, a diver who has seen the world a dozen times and still come back for more, but with a few drinks in him he became, well, sentimental.

'You ought to take it out, Jon,' he said.

'Take what out?'

I was at another table and I hadn't really followed what was happening.

'The wood,' he said, gesturing to the beggar, who was by now half off his skateboard and slumped against the wall.

'Oh man, no.'

I could see this getting really difficult. 'That's a job for a surgeon. Besides, we're not equipped.'

'You were saying not an hour ago that the hospital is one of the best that you've worked in.'

'Well yes. It is. But . . .'

'You can't do it?'

'Look. I could probably get the thing out. After all, it can't be through anything important or he'd be dead by now.'

'Well, let's do it.'

'He needs a hospital.'

'You're in India now, mate. If you don't treat him no one will.'

The mood had shifted a bit. It was still playful but they were, after all, relying on me to treat them if the worst should happen. Under the playfulness the test of confidence was real enough.

Gerry, beside me at the table in the shadows, whispered, 'Give it a try for Christ's sake.'

By now the beggar had so much drink inside him that nothing short of the last trump would have disturbed him, so I took my first close look at the problem. It was rod-shaped, almost a dowel, and it was thrust deeply under the pectoral muscle group on both sides. There was skin reddening around the wounds but very little inflammation. As far as I could see it would only need infiltration with an anaesthetic and then a gentle firm tug.

We took him, semi-conscious, back to the ship and the whole British dive crew gathered in the small operating area to watch. Suddenly I was much more sober than any of the rest of them. Removing these objects is usually uncomplicated, but I remembered a story that I had been told in training, of a child who had been brought into an accident hospital with a car ornament embedded in his skull. He was conscious and normal aside from that, so the houseman anaesthetised the scalp and pulled the object out. The patient died in minutes from an uncontrollable bleed. The ornament had acted as a plug.

I bared the beggar's chest. By now he was deeply unconscious and breathing with his mouth open. He had perhaps three blackened teeth. The rest were nubs. His tongue and cheeks were stained from chewing betel.

Close to, the job looked much easier than I had expected. There was healing at the skin edges and little adhesion to the rod. I infiltrated a little saline at each end and gave a very tentative pull. The rod slid neatly out, covered in a slippery viscous exudate. The crew watched open-mouthed.

'Just like that,' said Dave. Gerry grinned and made a triumphant 'O' with his fingers and thumb.

I cleaned the skin edges and packed the wound with gauze and dry antibiotic powder. This wound looked like nothing that I'd ever seen before. The tunnel that the object had left was smooth and clean, no infection, let alone bleeding. There was a general murmur of approval. I felt I had passed the test.

We took the beggar on deck to recover in the fresh air and left him with his skateboard beside him wrapped in a borrowed blanket. In the morning both beggar and blanket were gone.

Two weeks later I was taken via a hair-raising ride on the back of the base manager's Honda to discuss our gas requirements with our supplier in Bombay.

There, at the same intersection, riding the same vivid green skateboard, was our beggar, and through his chest, protruding on both sides, was another dowel!

I pointed him out to the base manager who explained that my former patient was a Hindu holy man of sorts. 'They go in for things like that to demonstrate they've gone through the pain barrier,' he explained with conspicuous lack of enthusiasm for the idea.

'But how?'

'At the beginning they cut and lift the chest muscles with hooks and then they push the rod that you see there through. They smear it with herbs so as to close the bleeding off and to stop infection. They take it out each night. It's a bit of nonsense to rip off the devout.'

The lights changed and we roared off into the mêlée of autorickshaws and taxis, horn blaring, ignoring the old man who sat on his green skateboard and watched the traffic and called 'Halah,' in a flat monotonous voice.

* * *

We were a week in Nhava base before we were ready to go to sea. During all that time we never actually saw Bombay except as a distant, blue-hazed city far off across the bay. A long finger of causeway reached out to a multi-minaretted mosque on its island, and occasionally, if the wind was right, the lonely, keening call of the Muezzin, summoning the faithful to pray, drifted across to us.

The night before we were due to sail we had an official shore leave, official, that is, in that a boat was laid on to take us across the bay by sea to the city.

The launch dropped us at a quay near the Gateway to India, its imposing bulk shining faintly yellow under the sodium lamp illumination.

Gerry negotiated with a Sikh taxi driver and we set off for Leopold's, the main expat hangout in Bombay. Once a vegetable market, before that, the old timers will tell you, a house of ill repute, nowadays its food is an institution, good and plentiful and very very cheap. It was the run-up to the elections in India, and the sale of

drink was officially banned throughout the city so as not to inflame
feelings. But in Leopold's they solved the problem by serving jugs
of beer rather than bottles and pouring it into the tall stainless steel
beakers usually used for water in India.

This subterfuge would hardly have fooled a child, but the two
policemen on guard at the street corner seemed happy enough. I
learned quickly that in India it is the appearance that counts.

We ate a splendid meal watching all around us India flow by in a
great rich river of sensation.

'We'll go to the Fire Temple after,' said Gerry, sipping his beer
and watching the antics of an old blind man, who was charming a
lethargic looking cobra.

'I thought that the Parsees didn't encourage visitors.'

'They don't. But I know the local priest. I nearly became a Parsee
once you know.'

I was surprised. Gerry had never struck me as a devout man.

I said, 'You're kidding me.'

'No. When I first came here I was going with this girl. She was
Parsee and so . . .' He broke off, and then, after a moment he
added, 'It was a long time ago. Long before I met up with Sue,
I was young then.'

'I don't know a lot about the Parsees, aside from the burial rites
of course.'

'Oh yeah. The Towers of Silence. We can go there too if
you like, but there's not much to see, apart from the carrion
birds.'

The temple was a huge imposing building from the outside, but
it seems inward looking, as if its builders built to conceal some
great inner secret. Entering through two great bronze doors was
like stepping into another time. There were torches everywhere,
thick heavy blue smoke from the sandalwood, and a great vaulted
ceiling that stretched so high that the light did not penetrate its
vaults. And there was something else, a sense of peace.

We stayed there a while, not talking, not moving, simply looking
at the temple, at the carvings, at nothing, and feeling that strange
sense of serenity.

An old man came across to us and steepled his hands in the gesture
of welcome that you find throughout India. The incense smoke roiled
and wafted around us. Through the blue haze, I fancied that I saw
shapes, almost an image, that flickered like a mirage and was gone

before it had time to register. Gerry shook his head as if he had awakened from sleep.

'We should be going,' he said. 'There is a place I know where they play traditional music. You'll enjoy it.'

'OK.'

He looked at me. Then as if he had decided after long deliberation he said, 'What did you see in the smoke, Jon?'

'Nothing. Shadows. The light of the torches.'

'They say that each man can see his future there if he looks closely enough.'

'Gerry,' I said, hoping to turn this strange mood of his, 'you have been in India too long.'

But there had been a picture in the smoke. A ship. A ghostly wraith of a ship, settling deep in the water, as if she were sinking.

Outside on the street the beggars were still patrolling their patch of pavement, calling endlessly, Halah . . . Halah.

I dismissed the image. Incense smoke and the flickering fires had been all that it was. That and the overwhelming sense of spirituality about that place.

Beyond the temple the Tower of Silence loomed dark against the sky. The Parsees, believing the elements of earth, air, water and fire to be sacred, dispose of their dead by exposing the bodies within the hollow Tower for the birds to take.

Gerry flagged down a taxi and we ended the night listening to long, liquid runs on sitar and tabla, far into the night. But in the launch, as we travelled back across the bay, cutting a phosphorescent wake of disturbed marine animals through the dark water, I could not help returning in my mind to the Fire Temple and the fleeting image of a sinking vessel that I had seen through the smoke from the torches.

7

We were in the far north of the Bombay High Field on a day so calm that it seemed that the monsoon was no more than a distant memory.

That far away from the main body of the oil-bearing dome that underlies a long section of the west coast of India there are few platforms and fewer pipelines. We were there more or less by chance. In a set of circumstances that could only happen in India we were diverted from our normal field of operations to deliver a gas analyser to our sister vessel which happened to be way up in the north.

Really it was a job that should have been carried out by helicopter. The analyser was a small instrument weighing perhaps eight or nine pounds, but it was Diwali, the beginning of the Hindu festival of lights, and somehow there was no helicopter available. We were eighty miles or so from our rendezvous in mid-ocean when the distress call came in.

A supply boat, another unlucky, diverted straggler in this normally quiet patch of ocean, had struck a submerged wreck and torn a hole in the plates of her bottom. While she was not exactly sinking, the water was coming into the ship faster than the pumps could force it out again and that of course was a circumstance with only one possible outcome. We were requested to divert to her assistance as soon as possible.

Despite popular fiction it takes a long time for a ship to sink in the open sea. True, there are the unlucky exceptions who are overtaken by giant waves, but usually a sinking ship gives time to clear life-rafts and a chance to save the crew.

Questioned on the radio, the skipper of the supply boat thought it would not come to that.

'I have excellent pumps running already,' he said.

'But you do require assistance?'

'Yes indeed, I am requiring help.'

Andy, our Scots skipper, favoured the handset with a despairing glance. He said, 'Can you confirm that you are not in danger at the present?'

'Indeed yes. But shortly I shall be.'

We were gathered on the bridge, standing in a group in the exit of the radio room. Andy keyed the mike as if to make a further comment then relaxed and put it back on the desk.

'It's no bloody good,' he said. 'It's always the same. He doesn't want to commit himself on the air in case the bloody owner's listening.' He thought for a moment then said, 'Right, we best have all the emergency crews ready as required for a full turn-out.'

As skipper it was Andy, rather than Gerry, who took command when the ship was in emergency role.

I said, 'Has he got any casualties?'

'No. At least none that he's mentioned.'

'OK.'

Preparing the ship for her emergency role is an exercise in controlled chaos. We all have dual functions in this kind of situation, but we also had six divers in the system and they had still to be looked after and kept informed as we worked. The deck, normally cleared to allow the landing of heavy sections of equipment, was littered with emergency pumps and firefighting gear.

The pumps used for this kind of work are small and air driven, as opposed to the usual electric drive, or the heavier diesels. Air drives are of course totally water proof and require only the passage of a high pressure air line to run them as long as we have our compressors. Down in the depths of the ship we pumped the huge steel Kelly bottles of air up to their maximum pressure. Running out of air during a rescue would not be appreciated. We were not exactly unsure of the strength of our locally tested Kelly tubes, but there was a collective sigh of relief when they reached the maximum pressure without any untoward happening.

The casualty looked OK. She was a long-hulled, dirty, rusty, black and yellow vessel and, aside from wallowing in the water rather deeper than usual, there was no sign that she was in trouble. We passed a pair of steel towing lines so that the air lines would bear no strain if the vessels moved apart, and then the pumps were hoisted up into a sky the colour of a black tulip and swung across. It was a textbook operation for at least the first two hours. The pumps fired up, the water spewed over the side in a steady stream. We all gathered on the deck to watch and then it all went wrong.

The squall was not really so terrible. It came screaming in out of the dark in a gust of drenching rain, and the sea that had been dark and slow and lazy was suddenly white and foamy and running in all directions at once. The steel towing bridle, designed only to hold a gentle swell, pulled suddenly bowstring tight. Even then there might have been no real problem if the casualty had not started her engines in a great belch of smoke, churned the sea to foam in her wake, and steamed directly away from us as hard as she could.

Andy was taken unawares by this bit of independent action. His gentle, steady, pull into the wind was suddenly countered by the drastic violent haul from behind. To avoid being dragged directly on to the smaller ship he could only pull back, and at that point the towing hawser decided that enough was after all enough, snapped with a crack like an artillery shell, and whipped in both directions.

There are many horror stories of the damage that a broken wire can do to anyone unlucky enough to be hit by one. Fortunately, this wire whistled across our deck and missed the whole crew, doing no more damage than slicing an empty mineral water bottle neatly in half. That however was as far as our good luck was to go.

The weather, having closed down on us, stayed bad. The sea was rising almost as fast as we could take in the situation, and the still, tropical night was, by now, a shrieking nightmare. The casualty was some half a mile off. His engine was running still, but he was no longer making way. The vital air line to the pump was of course severed along with the hawser. As we watched, the lights on the other ship flickered, dimmed, and went out.

Gerry was beside me in the lee of the welding shop, a position that allowed us a clear view out over the stern.

'Oh Christ, he's lost power,' he said.

'Water again, do you think?'

'I suppose. How the hell are we going to pass a line in this?'

'God knows. Also the synflex line for the pumps is a wreck. I'll have to make up another one.'

'How long is that going to take?'

'Half an hour, maybe more. If we can recover the old line I might be able to put a junction in it at the break.'

'But it'll be stretched won't it? What if it bursts?'

'It's all I can do.'

We were recovering the bright orange flexible air line from the sea, when Andy came down with even worse news.

'Look, we've got real trouble.'

'Yeah, we know.'

'No, just a minute. He's taking water fast and he can't hold position without power. That would be bad enough, but when the squall hit the chief was down below.'

'I just know I'm not going to like this,' I put in.

'You might just be right there. He's injured and trapped by the leg.'

'What? In the engine room?'

'That's right.'

'In a sinking ship?'

'Give the man a cigar. The skipper wants to know, if it gets to it, can you take his leg off?'

'No.'

'Just like that?'

'I'm not a bloody surgeon. It can't be done.'

'They did it in Nelson's day.'

'They all died in Nelson's day, too. Look, I'll go across to him. I'll try to help him out, but there's no way I can do that.'

The Zodiac transfer was a nightmare. It was not the motion of the little rubber boat so much as the total lack of horizon. The world was all black-green water and churning foam. Twice I nearly lost the vital emergency pack over the side. In a minute we were wet through, in two, soaked in sea water. They followed us with the big searchlight from the bridge, creating an island of light around us in the sea. It was little comfort. All I could think about was the stainless steel saw in the kit. I had slipped it in along with the rest of the gear, saying nothing about it to Gerry. It was brand new, never used, with a straight cold steel handle like a carpenter's tenon saw. I had never used such a surgical tool in my life and the thought of using it now scared me even more than the sea around me.

The ship loomed in front of us out of the murk. She was a dead steel bulk, the only lights on her deck torches and emergency beacons. She was very low in the water already. Our landing was easy. There was a ring of frightened faces on the deck around us, white eyes pale against dark golden skins, everyone in international rescue orange. I hate that colour.

The boatswain led Gerry and me below decks. The plan was that the Zodiac would begin to transfer the crew while we worked. The deck radio crackled and barked orders. Presently Andy's voice came clear across the sea from the safe haven of the *Sevak*.

'Do you hear me, lads?'

Gerry keyed his mike. 'Yes, go ahead.'

'If the shit hits the fan I'll give you a few minutes to get clear. If I call you out you come right away.'

'Roger that.'

We followed dark passageways deep in the ship. There was the smell of Indian food, of incense, of sandalwood. In the torch beams a garish printed poster of Ganesha, the elephant-headed god of good fortune, caught the light.

The deeper we went the more the ship felt claustrophobic as if she might at any time slip into the water. The engine-room bulkhead doors were dogged tight. The steel casing was screwed close to the framing with stainless steel bolts. As we opened it, a gust of air, heavy with the engine-room smells of oils and sweat, gushed out. That was bad. The increase in air pressure could only have come from water forcing its way in lower down.

We clambered down slippery spiderwork catwalks, thick with the oily breath of the diesels. It was deadly quiet down there. In what was normally the noisiest place on the ship there was now only the faint insistent lapping of water and the quiet moans of a man in pain.

He was twelve feet clear of the water level, trapped on a steel deckplate by a collapsed I-beam that had crushed his right leg below the knee and pinned him neatly to the deck. There was blood on the dirty green of the steelwork, very bright and red in the torch light. Gerry cracked a morphine syrette while I went to work on the leg.

Trapped patients are a special problem quite apart from the physical hazards of entrapment. When a limb is caught for long periods of time the muscle dies, and, if the blood supply to it is restored, the products of the dead meat flush back into the living body, overwhelming the kidneys and liver. It is a cruel phenomenon, forgotten between disasters and rediscovered as each new occasion calls it forth again like a forgotten murderer come to leer from the shadows and find fresh victims.

To find a pulse was important. A leg with a pulse at the ankle has a blood supply, its muscles are vital, it is a limb that can be saved. Without a pulse even my butchery could do no harm to the limb.

I felt the ankle above the grey cotton sock. It was slippery and tacky with blood. There was no pulse. I ran my fingers deeper feeling for the ridge of the Achilles' tendon, pressed in, and there it was, faint but thready.

I said to Gerry, 'I've got a pulse. The leg's alive.'

'Shit.'

'I can't take it off for God's sake. If it were dead I'd try, but now . . .'

'His bloody leg's going to be no good to him at the bottom of the Indian Ocean.'

The patient was out cold by now. The morphine had done its work.

I said, 'Look. If it gets to that, I think we should give him another two syrettes.'

'Jesus. You won't cut into his leg but you'd kill the poor bastard.'

'I can't take off his leg. That's no reason to leave him awake while the water rises.'

Gerry looked at the I-beam.

'If I can shift this a moment, it'll only be a moment, can you get him clear?'

'No problem. But it must weigh a ton and we've no power.'

There would be a chain hoist up above us in the steelwork to lift bearing caps and so on, but this beam would be well outside its lift capacity. Gerry shone his torch up and two decks above us in the spidery catwalks above the engine room it picked out a loop of chains and a block.

As Gerry was hoisting it across I shone a light down. The water was swirling down there. It was dark and filthy with debris, rags and emery-cloth and chunks of wood, even a dead ship's rat that had somehow forgotten to abandon the ship in advance. The chain rattled downwards.

We looped it around the beam. It was nowhere near heavy enough, but it would have to do. He pulled on the loop. The chain rattled across the pulley head. The lift came taut, slipped a little, came taut again and shifted the beam a fraction. The patient began to scream. Gerry hesitated.

I shouted, 'Go on, for God's sake. He'll have to take it. There's no time.'

The beam swayed and shifted. I could hear it grinding against steel, against flesh, against bone. We gained a quarter-inch.

The ship groaned somewhere in her guts. A half-inch. The man was silent now. Two inches, and the steel edge was clear of his flesh. Regardless of the pain I hauled him clear.

Gerry took one arm, I took the other, and we half dragged, half carried him up the companionway, along the catwalk, through the watertight door, and into the deserted corridor. The deck radio was chattering away but we were too hyped up to care.

As we passed the poster of Ganesha, Gerry crossed to it and pressed his palms together in the Indian gesture of greeting.

'I didn't know that you believed in all that,' I said.

'I didn't, but some bastard helped us tonight.'

Inside her the ship groaned again, and lurched a little, too heavy with water to recover properly.

'Time we were gone.'

Andy was on the deck and the *Sevak*, wonder of wonders, was alongside, despite the seas. The deck was nearly awash. He said, 'What kept you buggers? Trying for overtime again?'

We loaded the injured man on the basket and whisked gently through the air, back to the safety of our own deck space.

* * *

The weather, having done its worst, moderated fast. It had been one of those short lived, violent, tropical disturbances that plague shipping in the warmer oceans of the world.

In the hospital the injured man was sleeping, under heavy sedation. There was very little more that I could do for his leg at that stage. It was gashed deeply, and bruised nearly black over most of the skin surface, but the edges of the wound were red rather than the dirty grey of dead tissue, and the blood supply was intact.

I cleaned the wound up, dousing it with peroxide to ward off tetanus, always a problem in India, and covered the cut with a clean padded dressing. In the time that we had been fighting to get the man off the sinking ship a helicopter had set out from Bombay and there was really nothing else to do but wait to medevac him.

The ship, with the perversity of her kind, was hanging on to the last hours of her life. The damage to her hull was too great to allow safe access and it had been decided that we were to stand by until she sank rather than attempt salvage.

There is something about a shipwreck that draws spectators. I suppose we all know that, in the end, the sea will always have the last word, but to see it happen, to watch the water creep gradually over the open space of the aft deck and finally to see the hulk roll to show her weed-fouled underside and dull gleaming prop to the sun one last time before she started the mile deep plunge to the bottom, that was an experience filled with unexpected emotion.

Presently the sea settled itself down and the bubbles stopped rising. There was nothing to show but a few insignificant scraps of debris floating in an oily scum on the surface.

Our injured man was long gone by then, trundled away in the ungainly Aeroflot helicopter towards the beach, Bombay, and amputation. There were really no facilities for anything else.

Gerry turned back from the rail. The sun was going down on the horizon and the brief period of twilight was upon us.

'Back there in the ship,' he said, 'if we'd had to. Would you have cut him?'

'I don't know. I know the theory but I've never been trained to do it in practice. The shock would have killed him I think.'

'So what kept you there, mate, when we thought she was sinking?'

'He needed us. Isn't that what all the training is about?' I was embarrassed to be forced to spell it out.

'Yeah.' But Gerry sounded less than convinced. He changed the subject. 'You going home on the twentieth?'

'Sure, our six weeks is up then. Aren't you?'

'I'm not so sure I've got much to go home to.'

'What? How about Sue and the kids.'

'The kids might care.'

'Things not so good then?'

'Recently it's as if she's glad to see me go.'

'Look, mate,' I said, 'I don't want to butt in, but when I've been at home and you were away she talks about you all the time. She misses you, for Christ's sake.'

'Sure she does. But the strain is getting to her.'

'You being away, you mean?'

'Doing shit jobs like that one, I mean.'

'Well, it wasn't really that risky. Not enough to worry about.'

'You're getting as bad as me, mate. Jon, do me a favour?'

'What?'

'I got you into this. I didn't mean to get you bloody killed. Don't start taking risks, mate. It gets so that you like it in the end.'

8

We had just two weeks to work to complete our contracts and those were to be the last two weeks that any of us were to spend in India, at least on that ship, for we were being replaced one by one as we came due for leave with basic qualified raw recruits, all Indian nationals newly out of diving school.

Gerry and I left the ship together and spent our last night in Leopold's eating rich Indian food and drinking cold Hindustani Breweries beer.

'Well,' said Gerry, breaking a pause in the conversation, 'where now?'

'I hear that there's work in the South China Sea.'

'Too many accidents in that field, mate. No thanks. How about the North Sea?'

'Maybe,' I said. 'There's a lot of new construction off the east side.'

A new arrival joined us at the table, sat down without asking in the familiar way of expats in India, and said, 'You gentlemen divers?'

'Sure.'

'Paid off?'

'In the morning.'

'Are you interested in working in Singapore?'

And with that we were fed, watered, hired and contracted, all without leaving Leopold's restaurant.

* * *

Gerry and I did not see each other for a while after getting home. Working so closely together, relying so much on each other, we do not seek out each other's company for a few weeks after a job. When I did see him again, five weeks after we had left Bombay, Gerry had news for me.

'I got the details of the Singapore job today,' he said.

Outside it was autumn with a chill wind blowing that sliced

through the crevices of the buildings to find its icy way into the warmth inside.

Singapore, the tropics and the fabled South China Sea seemed a million miles away.

'Yes,' I said. 'So are you going to tell me or what?'

'Well, I'm the boss and there's a mate of yours on the team as well.'

'Who would that be?'

'Old Billy Carson.'

'Oh God.'

'Hey, he likes you.'

'Then he's got a bloody funny way of showing it.'

'He said you had the balls of a tiger.'

'You're making that up.'

'No. True. Look, you have him all wrong. He's a nice guy but he doesn't like amateurs.'

'Thanks.'

'That's not what I meant. When you first started you were an oddity, you being a graduate and all. Now it's different.'

'Because of that business on the crane?'

'Not just that. But at least it proved you can do the job.'

'Fair enough. Where exactly are we going?'

'Well, it isn't Singapore as such. It's down in Malaysia. He'll tell you about it next week.'

'Who will?'

'Billy Carson. He's project boss and he's coming to see me on Friday, so get your drinking boots on.'

'I can hardly wait.'

Normally I am as sociable as most, but the thought of spending an evening drinking with Billy Carson at Gerry's place wasn't my idea of fun.

Our wives also decided that the evening would not be one of the world's all-time great social events, and took themselves off to our house, a matter of three hundred yards or so down the road, for refuge.

Billy looked just as I had remembered him. The same hook-nosed face, the same tanned leathery skin, and the same whipcord muscles on all the bits of him that showed.

He was sitting in front of Gerry's fire with a glass in his hand and Gerry's black retriever curled against his legs.

He looked up as I walked into the room.

'Well now, youngster,' he said, 'how are you enjoying it, now that you know what it's all about?'

It wasn't all that incongruous actually. He was maybe twenty years older than me.

'It's all I expected and more,' I replied.

He nodded as if this was what he had expected. 'Aye, and now you know it all?'

'No, just a bare beginning.'

Gerry passed me a drink. 'We were talking about the odd things that happen sometimes,' he said.

'Odd?' I queried.

'Aye, when you've a few more years in you'll understand.' Billy switched the subject abruptly to the upcoming job. Three hours and a good deal of rum later, Billy finally told the story that he had been about to tell Gerry when I had interrupted them.

By then something odd had indeed happened. Despite all my prejudices against him, I was getting to like old Billy Carson. What in another man might have been false machismo was in him the simple truth. If he seemed tough it was because he was tough. But of all the stories that he told me during the period of our friendship, and there were many of them, none was stranger than the one he told that first night with Gerry's gas fire hissing and bubbling to itself and the old black dog snoozing at his feet.

*　　*　　*

'We were off Norway,' he said, 'and there was a cruel gale blowing. It was aboard a ship, not a semi-sub, and there was nothing left to do but run into the waves and wait for the weather to blow itself out. That was one hell of a storm. It blew solid for three days and nights and by the third day a good few of the crew were sick and incapable.

'The medic tried all the usual stuff, but still, with the ship corkscrewing the way they do, and the smell of oil coming up from below, it was hard to keep food down. In the end it got to the point where the marine crew were standing double watches, so a few of us on the dive team who had been on trawlers relieved them for a watch on the bridge.'

Billy rolled a home-made smoke and looked at us to see that we were listening. We were and he continued.

'The deck was washed through time after time. I saw the gas quads go, and it was pure luck that they were washed clean over, rather than charging around the deck and smashing something.

'We were about an hour into the watch and all you could see outside through the clearscreen was water tearing every which way. It was all white and greeny black, the way it gets in really bad weather. My mate was keeping an eye to the middle-distance radar because visibility wasn't worth a shit. We could have rammed a cathedral in the dark before we had known it was there. Anyhow he suddenly calls out, "Ship dead ahead three miles."

'Well, I shifted course a few points to bring us well away from her. Steering in such weather you need searoom. She altered her motion a bit too, with just that little shift, and that shows you how bad the weather was.

'We held course for a while and, as you can imagine, I was looking out through the clearscreen as best I could for her lights. I asked my mate about the radar picture but he'd lost it in the scatter. Well that was OK. In those conditions the wave tops interfere with radar and it's easy to lose things, even things the size of a ship. But for all we knew she might have shifted course too, so it was an uneasy sort of time.

'After an hour or more with still nothing on the screen and no sighting, I was thinking that maybe the radar had screwed us up. Then suddenly she was right in front of me, but the thing was she wasn't a ship but a platform, with all her lights blazing and her proximity warnings sounding.

'I sheered off as best I could but we were already deadly close and for a moment or two I was afraid that I'd lose the ship in the wave troughs. But she was kind, and she righted herself in a moment or two.

'By then I was over the fright enough to be bloody angry and I turned to bollock my mate on the radar when I saw his face. He was really scared. Now this is a guy who has been in some tough places. He's no baby, but he's sitting there as white as a sheet. I thought that it was maybe the near miss that had done it and it didn't seem as if bollocking him would do either of us any good, so I left him be and held course.

'For a long time he said nothing, and no one came to check on the sudden shift of course. Maybe they put it down to the storm blowing her about, and it wasn't until after we were safe off watch that I mentioned it to him.

'I said, "That was too bloody close for comfort."'

'Ane he said, "Yes."'

'That's all. Just "Yes", and then he shut up. Well, I thought that he was afraid I'd give him shit over the radar so I said, "It's easy to miss things in the scatter, mate, especially on a night like this."'

'Now that was fairer than it ought to have been because a platform is like a bloody lighthouse the way it sticks up, and there isn't any way that you should miss it, scatter or no. But he still said nothing. I thought, "Well, bugger you then" and I went to bed.

'The next day it was quieter. The weather was all blown out, and we put ourselves into Stavanger to check for damage. We were in the bar of the Dickens when he told me what I'd missed seeing while I was fighting the ship around. It was like this. What he saw was not just a platform where no platform had a right to be, but a five-legged platform. Now that's an obsolete design especially in that sector.

' "It was the *Kielland*," he said. "As clear as I see you now." '

The atmosphere in Gerry's sitting-room was suitably chilled by then. Billy yawned and shifted. The old dog grunted his protest.

Production platform *Alexander Kielland* had been destroyed in a storm off Norway with great loss of life years before. Until the *Piper Alpha* it had been the world's worst oil disaster.

Gerry reached for the bottle and poured.

'I reckon this will be one for the road,' said Billy, and ten minutes later he was gone into the chilly autumn night.

'I told you he had a story or two to tell,' said Gerry, seeing me out in my turn.

Back at home I tried, without success, to convey the atmosphere of menace in Billy's account to my wife.

'Ghost stories for heaven's sake,' she said. 'Three grown men telling themselves creepy stories to scare themselves stupid. So much for the North Sea Tigers.'

9

War rarely touches the deep-sea diving industry, but 1991 was a year that a war was fought for oil and, as the year turned, Saddam Hussein's insane adventure in Kuwait had the whole industry poised waiting for the inevitable strike in retaliation and the reconstruction work this would bring in its train. So Singapore went on a back burner while the operators hung on for the prospect of rich contracts and long-term work closer to home.

Such a strategy was all well and good for the operations managers secure on their regular salaries in Aberdeen, but for the personnel involved the situation was very different.

Finally, after delaying as long as I dared, I took a short-term job in Norway, expecting it to be completed well before there was work to do in the Gulf.

'At least,' said Gerry, when I told him that I was flying out the next day, 'no one will be trying to kill you in Norway.'

But in that, as in a good deal else that year, he was wrong.

Normally, the nearest the deep-sea diving industry gets to war is disposing of the rusted relics of ancient conflicts or the chance discovery of uncharted wrecks. At the end of the First World War in the climate of revulsion that followed the endless bloodletting it was decided that some whole classes of weapons were to be forever banned. As a result old stocks of mustard gas, and the early nerve agents tabun and sarin, were destroyed, never to be resurrected. Sadly the Second World War called old skills and old technologies back into action though, of course, with a few accidental exceptions the weapons were never used.

Later, in the euphoria of the peace, old stocks, as in 1918, were destroyed. Sadly, though, things had moved on in twenty-five years. The destruction of the newer chemicals was a problem in itself. They were hard to burn, and chemically stable, and to make things more difficult they were also developing a nasty tendency to leak, so as a matter of public record, in 1946, eight ancient hulks were loaded with the most dangerous cargo that mankind had ever produced, taken out to sea and scuttled. As to where at sea this act of conspicuous idiocy took place, that was not a matter of public record.

Like most of those who work the North Sea, I was aware of those hulks, though I never expected them to be a problem.

We were carrying out a routine ploughing operation. Pipelines, like everything else made by man, wear out, and new pipes, when they are laid, are extruded in a continuous welded run from a lay barge and allowed to settle gently to the bottom. Having settled, and been tested, they are then vulnerable to trawler skippers who ignore the fact the pipes are marked on every marine chart and haul nets across them. To safeguard the lines, the environment and the oil and gas that they carry, we bury them, and to do that we use the plough.

It looks much like an ordinary land-going single-share plough, but this monster is thirty feet high, and pulls a furrow on the seabed wide enough to drive a Mini through.

So we were ploughing gently along the pipeline. The divers, six in sat, were relaxed and well rested and, as is their wont when relaxed and rested, they were making life tough for the topside crew with constant requests for hot drinks, for dry towels, for reading matter, for snacks, even for a twenty-minute gossip, and that's maybe the toughest job of all when every word is strained and mangled and distorted by a helium unscrambler.

It was towards the end of a shift, about eleven thirty at night, when the phone rang.

'Sat control,' I said.

'Radio room. I've just picked up a medevac request from a trawler.'

'Is nobody else handy?'

'Well, we're the nearest.'

This is a situation that happens all too often, and mostly at the end of a shift. It means a rough transfer in a shimmering little bubble of a helicopter and a drop on to the deck of a trawler. It also usually means little or no sleep. By the time the job is done it is time to take over the panel again. In other words a call at this time of day means thirty-six hours straight with no rest between.

'You're sure he needs a medevac?'

'He said one of his deck crew was burned.'

There is, for all of us, a call that we cannot ignore. Burns are that one thing I can't leave or pass on to someone else. Not after *Piper Alpha*.

I said, 'OK. I'll get the kit. Is Greg ready?'

'Warming up now.'

I pulled on the bright yellow survival suit over jeans and T-shirt. At that time of the year and that far north it was still light at midnight, the famous white nights of the Arctic Circle.

Greg, our stand-by pilot, was already in the Alouette. He learned to fly in the paddy-fields of Vietnam and some of his methods are combat expedients, but he can put the chopper down in conditions that are very near to the edge of impossible and through all the banter he is the best pilot on the job, bar none.

He motioned me to put on the headset.

'You-all working overtime?'

'No choice.'

'They could have got a team in from Stavanger.'

'No. Three hours minimum to get them together and on site. We can be there in what?'

'Twenty minutes. You-all ready?'

'As ready as I'll ever be. Can you set down on her?'

'A trawler? Man, you must be joking.'

'We don't have a winch.'

'I'll hover at zero feet. You'll jump.'

'As long as it's zero feet.'

'No sweat. It's flat calm.'

The trawler was immediately in sight from a thousand feet, her navigation lights bright in the pale perpetual dawn of the high Arctic twilight. The sea was dead flat and as soon as we were in close range we could see that we had got our first stroke of luck; she had a helideck.

'Looks like you-all going to ride all the way to the job,' observed Greg, as if on the whole he disapproved of such pampering.

We put down neatly on the white H in the centre of the small floodlit circle of the helideck.

I climbed down, ducking, as everyone does, to clear the circle of the rotors, though from a sensible angle of approach there really is no need of any such precaution.

Two Norwegian seamen escorted me to a spotless sick bay where a man lay quiet on crisp white linen. His right arm was dressed to the shoulder in Roehampton dressings and his left hand was similarly swathed in non-stick padding.

His eyes held all the pain that I had expected.

The first instinct is to relieve that pain, but it's the wrong thing to do. First I had to find out the background. It is too easy to hide symptoms with well-intentioned medication.

'What happened?'

Either in pain or fright he had lost much of his English. His Norwegian was too fast for me to follow. I caught odd words, like straws in the gale of language.

'*Oyeblink* . . .' It happened quickly then. Well, it always does. There is never time to do more than react in those hot few moments when an emergency comes in out of nowhere and smashes the pattern of a peaceful working shift. Finally a huge man introduced himself as the skipper.

He said, 'He was hauling nets and in the net there was . . . I have no English word for it, a steel can of some sort, but heavy. We dropped it to the deck and there was oil on the steel. He touched it, picked it up, threw it into the sea, and then he began to scream. We went to help him and he was as you see. It was something from the can that did this thing to him.'

'Who dressed the injury?'

'I did. I hope that I have done right.'

'Of course, Captain. Entirely right. Look, I must examine the injury. Can you help me to take off the dressing?'

'Yes, but wear . . . hand covers.'

'Gloves?'

'*Ja*. Gloves.'

'Sure, we always do, but?'

He held out his hands palm up. They were the huge calloused hands of a man who had spent his youth working in salt water but, tough as the skin must have been, his palm was raised in a single fluid-filled blister that was capped with skin the texture of old leather.

'Jesus wept. You touched him and it did that?'

'*Ja*.'

'OK. I'll see to you after this is done. You say the container went back over the side?'

'*Ja* and the deck has been swabbed clean. There will be no more.'

'Good,' I said. But I was thinking that perhaps it was not so good. The one chance that we had of identifying that mystery canister was gone.

I pulled the dressing back, soft and easy. Roehampton dressings don't stick. They are safe to cover even the most terrible weeping burns and they will not lift skin from even the most damaged of blisters, but even so the injury beneath them was horrific.

The right arm was blistered from finger to shoulder, a single massive exudate of fluid that surrounded the limb like a grotesque carnival glove. There was no trace of heat, no charring, no blackened tissue, nothing but a faint, vaguely familiar smell that tickled mucous membranes and stung the back of my throat.

I covered the arm again. There was nothing to be done out there. This was a burns unit job, requiring débridement of dead tissue, open sterile dressing and skin grafting. But the smell worried me. I pressed the stethoscope against his chest wall. His heart sounds were OK but within his lungs, like a wave washing on a far shore, the tides of the man's breathing were congested and fluid-wracked.

I said, 'He needs a hospital right now. I can't even guess what he's been in contact with, but there's nothing to be done out here. Also he's inhaled something. His chest sounds rough. I want him into Stavanger and fast. Get your radio room to call our pilot in and tell him to move it.'

The captain passed on the orders in Norwegian. Then I motioned him to a seat.

'Pull up your shirt. Good. Now breathe. Hold it. Now again.'

It was fainter, but it was there. A whisper of fluid in the flow of air in his lungs.

'Right. You too.'

'Me too?'

'Medevac. I don't know what you've been in contact with, but whatever it is you need a check-up.'

There was a smell in his woollen sweater. On a trawler there is always the smell of fish but this was a sweet smell, a smell of cottage gardens and warm summer evenings in Cornwall. Roses? No, not quite.

'Rose geraniums,' I said aloud.

'What?'

'I'm sorry, I was thinking aloud. That smell. It was the stuff from the cylinder?'

'*Ja*, it smelled sweet like a lady, you know?'

'Perfumed, you mean?'

'*Ja*, perfumed but cheap perfume, you know?'

It was cramped in the helicopter on our way back to the beach. The captain was all for staying with his ship, but the injured man was showing increasing signs of respiratory distress and whatever evil substance had brought about this horrific injury was clearly still active. To take a chance with the one other victim who was showing clear signs of exposure was not prudent.

We landed at a quiet corner of Stavanger International Airport and transferred to a bright yellow ambulance with the blue snake and staff on the side.

Right from the moment that we reached the hospital things took on a dreamlike, detached quality that sometimes interposes itself in emergencies, once events get a momentum of their own. Our two casualties were whisked away and I was shunted into an empty cubicle, much like the ones where I gained my own early experience among the mangled RTA victims in casualty. After a time a technician wheeled in a vitalograph to test my lung function. It was of course normal.

A long time after, a young Norwegian doctor came in. He looked the way we all look when we have bad news to pass on.

He said, 'You are the medic?'

'Yes.'

'Well, it was not your fault. There was nothing to be done before you ever reached him.'

'He is dead?'

'Yes. They didn't tell you? I'm sorry. We were busy with the other one.'

'But for Christ's sake, what was it?'

'Fluid accumulated in his lungs.'

'Yes. I realise that, but there was very little fluid two hours ago. At least I found very little.'

'Well, facilities offshore are limited.'

'Not so limited that a man drowns in his own juice and we don't notice. What was he exposed to?'

'I don't know. At least not for sure.'

'No, but you have a fair idea. Look, I'm not trying to tie you down. This is not a court, but I need to know. Suppose it should happen again?'

'I'm sorry, I really can't tell you for certain what happened yet.'

At that moment the answer popped into my mind, the connection between that smell and a long-forgotten bit of information.

As a kid I had driven each weekend to the north coast of Cornwall and there I spent my weekends, haunting the surfing beaches, watching the waves, listening to the music. There, high above the cliffs at Portreath was a very odd government installation, an outstation of the Chemical Warfare Plant at Porton Down. People talked very little about Nancecuke at the time, and the place was closed amid suitable shudders of revulsion in 1976. Among the stories that did come out of it were accounts of the emergency drills.

At Nancecuke workers were taught how to recognise the chemicals by smell. Not the nerve gases of course, they are odourless in any case, but the others, the old compounds, among them nitrogen mustard with its faint sweet smell of rose geraniums.

I suddenly felt a long, long way out of my depth. I said to the doctor, 'It was mustard, wasn't it?'

'I'm sorry, I'm really not certain what it was.'

'Bollocks. You know what it was, and so do I. At least I think I do. It was dichlorethyl sulphide wasn't it?'

'No. Oh, perhaps. There's no way to be sure yet.'

'How many have there been?'

'A few. My government is already pressing those who dumped the stuff to move it, but I hardly need to point out the problems to you.'

'The man is dead. How much of that shit is down there?'

He shrugged. 'Come, we have a coffee.'

His room was better furnished than the cubicle. It was just short of luxurious. He poured fragrant black coffee and produced an unlabelled bottle of oily smooth spirit.

'Aquavit?'

'Please.'

'All right. There have been a number of cases over the last few years. You are right, at least in general terms. It is mustard gas or one of its relatives. Each time this happens the Navy sweeps the area and declares it clear. They warn the fishermen not to trawl in these spots, and then a few months later there is another incident.'

'But where does it come from?'

'Old stocks dumped at the end of the war. At the time it was thought that they would be safe enough.'

'But where were they dumped?'

'Officially no one is sure. The records were destroyed forty years ago or perhaps they weren't.'

'But surely the government would try to do something?'

'To do what? These things belong to no one. As I said, there are moves to have the sites cleared, but officially no one owns these wrecks. Perhaps the Allies dumped them, perhaps it was the Germans. Certainly there is no recorded wreck as such in that area.'

'So they have already looked?'

'Oh yes, I think so. Several times. But these things are scattered now and of course after so long in the sea the containers are leaking.'

'What will you tell the man's family?'

'The truth. We have an excellent social security system in Norway. They will be provided for.'

I sipped the coffee. There was the aromatic tang of aquavit in the steam that rose.

'So there is nothing to be done?'

'No. The existence of this material is known to a great many people. It is not secret, merely – how can I put it? – treated with discretion. If we could prove who owned the stuff, then of course they might just be handed the bill for a clean-up, but as it is . . .'

We spent the night in the triple-glazed comfort of the Scandic Hotel. I remember not sleeping too well. I had the persistent image of those old wartime hulks lurking in the dark waters, covered with concretation and rusticles as wrecks are after a while, but clean. No marine growths would encrust those wrecks, no fish would live in their yawning engine rooms, no crabs would crawl on the empty bridge. Instead they would wait, as they still wait, for the time when oxidation weakens the canisters enough to release their cargo to float, a lethal oily scum, to wherever the waves might take it.

It used to give me nightmares thinking about those old wrecks. At times it still does.

10

By the time I arrived home again from Norway the war against Saddam Hussein had reached its inevitable bloody conclusion on the road to Basra. The stir that the conflict had created throughout the relatively small community involved directly in oil production was, however, still spreading. Gerry came to see me within two days of my arriving home.

'You've got back just in time for the Big One,' he said.

'Kuwait you mean?'

'Of course Kuwait. Where the hell else? We are putting a team together to clear some of the ordnance.'

'We being who?'

'We being a company formed specially to do the job. The boss will be in touch in a few days. I put in a good word for you.'

'Great. Who else is going?'

'Billy Carson is in charge of the explosives side, the rest is Yanks and odd Brits with mine-clearing experience. I'm dive super.'

'I don't know, mate,' I said, 'I know damn all about ordnance.'

'No problem. All we need you to do is medic.'

'But it's a specialist field. You might be better off with an ex-RAMC medic.'

'Just see the man. OK?'

'OK.'

'It'll be good. You'll see.'

'Sure. Like hail after rain.'

'Yes, I hear that you had a bad one in Norway.'

'Bad enough. How's Sue?'

'Don't ask.'

'Bad?'

'Not good.'

'Oh, Gerry. Is it really a good idea to go to Kuwait then?'

'There's no real reason not to.'

Kuwait is one of those places that everyone involved in oil exploration visits eventually. It is one of the hot spots of our world, whose untold wealth in crude petroleum has transformed a poor feudal desert sheikhdom into a rich but equally feudal society. Not that the Kuwaitis as a whole were objecting. The ruling house was well spread enough, and well liked enough, for most of the population to feel that they had, as in the old times, a direct line to the court.

It is true that Kuwait was not a democracy, it was also true that the individual Kuwaitis, by and large, had very little interest in politics, as long as the wealth continued to flow.

Kuwait, as most of us remembered it before the invasion, was a land of startling, spotless modernism, grown out of the desert, and snuggled against the brilliant blue waters of the Gulf.

Very little of the oil industry of Kuwait was actually in local hands. Each project was nominally in the charge of a Kuwaiti national, but the gentleman who ran the first dive team we worked on there was amiable, keen to appear competent, and totally, abysmally ignorant of the techniques that we employ to keep us alive and working. It made for odd 'Alice in Wonderland' conversations where everybody was frantically trying to save his face, by saying nothing that might indicate the depth of his ignorance.

That was Kuwait. Amiable, rich, a little indolent, and spotless. But times have changed.

As Gerry had promised, it was not one of my usual contacts who put the job together. Alan, who was setting it up, rang me late one evening. He said there would be no saturation unless something went wrong.

'If there's no sat you really don't need me.'

'Well it could go to sat if the water turns out deeper than we thought. It'll be at a few places in the Gulf, all off Kuwait.'

'All right. I'm interested. What's the rate?'

He named a figure that made me immediately suspicious. One major pitfall of this industry is the 'get-rich-quick' companies offering dream tickets who emerge and vanish with the inevitability of hatching mayflies. I voiced my doubts.

'No. It's not like that. It's just a bit sensitive.'

'Sensitive? What are you talking about?'

'I'll be in your area next week. We could talk then. For now are you interested?'

'Yes. If it's legal.'

'Oh yes. It's legal.'

A week passed. Gerry had gone on ahead to mobilise the job. I felt less sure of the Kuwaiti project by the day.

Finally Alan turned up on my doorstep with a six-pack in one hand and a large briefcase in the other. He settled on to the sofa and cracked a beer.

He said, 'Nice place.'

'You've seen it before.'

'Yes.'

'About this sensitive job of yours.'

'Debris clearance, mate.'

'What the hell is sensitive about shifting junk off the bottom?'

'Did Gerry not tell you? Well, there's some funny stuff on the bottom out there.'

'You mean ordnance?'

'Right.'

'Do you have a team?'

'All ex-Navy clearance divers. They know their stuff.'

'Why don't the Navy sweep the area?'

'Resources, old mate. They need hired help, and we are it. Are you in?'

'All right, I'm in. But look, one thing. No official secrets crap.'

'Sure, tell who you like when the job's done.'

'How long will it run?'

'Six weeks. Maybe seven. You can afford to take the rest of the season off.'

'Oh, sure. When does it start?'

'Three days, OK? We need you to go over the system.'

'Fine.'

He grinned. 'Just one more formality. Sign this would you?'

'What is it?'

'Indemnity and Life Insurance. It says that you won't sue either the Kuwaitis, the Brits or the Yanks for that matter, and in return we will pay you one hundred thousand American dollars, if you get blown up.'

'That will be a great comfort.'

I read the document. It was what he said it was, so I signed it. Signing those releases always leaves you feeling as if you had articulated a death wish.

The flight from Heathrow was packed with a tough-looking bunch of expats going out to do business in the aftermath of the war, and a sprinkling of press and Arabs in flowing burnous and white headdresses.

As for the dive team, it is of course true that appearances don't count for a good deal, but that crew could have sailed with Bloody Morgan and not looked out of place. You can dress it any way you like, and say that they were 'rugged', or 'individualistic', but the fact is that, as a group, they looked as if they might well clear any bar of sensible customers by simply walking into it.

They gathered in a small isolated group in the departure lounge. I walked over to the one man I knew.

'Hello, Billy.'

'Jon by God. Is this going to go to sat then?'

'I don't know. They hired me as medic to start with.'

'Aye well. We'll no doubt be needing you.'

Now Billy knows explosives in the same dedicated fashion that I know diving medicine and he is very highly qualified in his own area. His opinions are worth respecting.

'This stuff we're clearing. How bad is it?'

'Laddie, it's built to be bad.'

'I see.'

'Don't worry. What this crew don't know about mines isn't worth knowing. Come on, I'll introduce you.'

It turned out that they weren't so villainous after all.

*   *   *

Kuwait was an Arabian fairytale no longer. From the moment the plane touched down evidence of the war was everywhere. The runways themselves had been cratered and roughly patched, and the military were in evidence wherever you looked. Either it was American troops, in casual uniform of desert buff, British troops, always much smarter in neat desert camouflage, or Kuwaiti nationals, looking infinitely more dangerous, with casually displayed AK 47 rifles and crossed bandoliers of ammunition.

The arrivals hall was once pure white, vaulted like a mosque, and cool with the chill kiss of air-conditioning. Now it was stiflingly hot, dirty, and poorly organised, with shell craters scarring the pure white vaults and cracks running throughout the masonry.

Security, once more or less relaxed in the Gulf, was suddenly tight.

Each of us was questioned by a Kuwaiti officer, with an American in plain clothes standing beside him.

'Your reason for visiting Kuwait?' he said.

'To work for your offshore oil authority.'

'You are an engineer? It does not say so on your visa.'

'I work for a diving company.'

'Just so. Have you any military connections in this area?'

'None.'

'This visa was issued by the Armed Forces Control Commission.'

'You would have to ask the company about that.'

'Others of your team are ex-members of the British Royal Navy.'

'Many divers are Navy-trained.'

'No other connection?'

'No. None at all.'

'Very well. Enjoy your stay.'

It took three hours for the whole team to clear the airport. Outside a bus was waiting, a number of ragged holes still pocking the aluminium panels of its bodywork. It was two in the afternoon, local time, and outside the airport there was twilight. The American who was our local liaison gestured to the dirty grey sky.

'Smoke,' he said, 'from the wells they set fire to. It never gets properly light now.'

Billy was sitting beside me on the bus. He grinned, and said, 'Reckon we could make a few quid after this is done, blowing wells out. Do you fancy it?'

'No. I don't really know enough about explosives.'

'It's easy, mate. You put enough in and the bugger goes out.'

The American picked up the microphone that tour guides had used to describe the delights of the city.

'Just a quick briefing, gentlemen, before you get to the hotel. The accommodation is a little rough, but you'll transfer offshore in the morning. Now tonight. Stay in the hotel. Don't wander the streets. There are patrols all the time, and if you can't account for yourselves you'll be in big trouble. There are still Iraqi deserters and stragglers about, and they get summary justice if they get caught. Don't mess with any interesting stuff you see lying about. Most of the souvenirs in the streets are mined and booby-trapped. A lot of the gear has been cleared, but just about all the trucks and tanks lying around might still have live charges attached, so stay off. In the morning you'll be transferred.

'Part of that trip will be by road. If for any reason we have to stop, stay in the area of the bus and don't wander about. All the sand, and I mean *all* of it, is scattered with AP mines. Oh, and forget that old shit about them not going off if you keep your weight on them. These are the latest Italian nasties, and they go off if you as much as fart near them. Enjoy your trip.'

The hotel was a wreck too. The top three floors were semi-rubble. The public rooms were in darkness, broken only by gas lamps. The fittings were mostly gone. There was a smell of terror about the place.

The man who served us food was terrified all right. You could read it in his gestures, in his eyes, in the nervous sweat that soaked through his roughly creased white uniform.

The American liaison manager explained. 'He's a Palestinian. When the Iraqis came, they were all ecstatic, thought the sun shone out of Saddam's arse. Well, that's what you get for backing the wrong side.'

'What do you get?' someone asked.

'Shot mainly. Every night you find that some of them are picked up and taken away. Some come back, some don't. The Palestinian quarter is like a ghost town at night. They hide, you see.'

Later that night, we heard the trucks rushing through the dark. And once, far away in the distance, a sharp rattle of small arms fire followed by a single crisp report. In the morning the waiter was gone.

The vessel was a modern DSV fresh from a refit in the shipyards of Cochin. We had all heard stories about the incompetence of the oriental yards but she looked trim and neat, and the dive system, a very nearly brand new Comex unit, was excellent.

We were allocated a cabin each and as always I was put next to the hospital. The first few days were like all such shakedown periods. Checking the supplies, running the dive system to 300 feet on air, curing the odd leak, preparing the hospital with the ready use equipment, suture kit, Roehampton dressings, IV sets for plasma and D5W. The stuff that saves lives in the first few minutes of treatment.

Each night we sat on deck in the warm air of the evening. The sky was an angry red shading to orange from the fires thirty miles away. It was not stargazing and relaxation that brought about this gathering – the smoke pall still effectively blocked the view in any case – but a briefing each evening on a different type of munition known to have been used in the area.

Our big worry was that it had been seeded with a particularly nasty Russian-made sea mine. Sea mines have come a long, long way since the old spherical floating charges with lead horns sticking out of them on all sides. The modern mine is controlled, like so much else, by a microprocessor, and is quite capable of executing a complex system of attack. It may sit inert, waiting for a particular signature from a ship's propeller, ignoring everything else. Or it is capable of allowing a preset number of vessels to pass before finally exploding in a game of high explosive Russian roulette.

Worse yet, these mines are intelligent about antihandling. They are the safest of all to lay, because the mine does not arm itself until some time after the laying vessel has long gone. But, once armed, approaching them with defusing equipment is very likely to cause an explosion. The approved method of coping with such a beast is to attach a cable, preferably by remote control, and tow it, and all those like it, into a safe area surrounding a large charge of plastic explosive. Having assembled this Devil's brew the plastic is fired and the remaining munitions sympathetically detonate. At least that was the theory and in theory it sounded so very simple.

During the Second World War mine-clearing crews had long obscene songs that they sang while they were on the job. At that time mine-clearance was boring, repetitive, and dangerous, relying as it did on torpedo-shaped floats that trailed long hanks of sharpened steel cable to sever the mooring cables of tethered mines so that they would float to the surface to be destroyed.

Nowadays, the cat and mouse game had altered. The Gulf War at sea was a very different affair to the Second World War. Drifting mines and random sown fields were not an effective means of attack by either side. But the installations themselves, the multi-million dollar platforms straddling the waters of the gulf like H. G. Wells' Martians, they were a different and more profitable target.

Even more than fires affecting land-based wells, fires at sea are desperately hard to control, and the pollution they can release is far and away more widespread and destructive. At the beginning of the end when the Iraqis were firing the land-based wells, some of the team had spent anxious days, waiting for the call to go and cap and seal a burning platform at sea, but the call had never come.

Now, with the war over, we were to examine that piece of apparent good fortune with more care, to see if, indeed, the platforms had been spared, or if they were simply a quietly ticking time bomb, waiting for the right moment to explode.

We started with an ROV survey of the first platform. The ROV is essentially a swimming TV camera that noses its way around the steelwork sending pictures back to the mother ship. Initially the idea was that the camera would survey much of the platform, freeing divers for the essential task of dismantling any charges that it might find.

Visibility was good, the water clear, like gin, tinged with blue right from the surface to the deep twilit zone down among the groupers and sea snakes. It was one of these that gave me my first problem, long before we encountered any war materials at all. There are sea snakes all over the warmer waters of the world and in the Gulf, for reasons only known to the reptiles themselves, they sometimes reach plague proportions. Individually they are handsome beasts, some eight feet long, and banded with shades of deep chocolate or black, shading off to vivid yellow stripes. They are in fact modified cobras, but they differ from their land-dwelling cousins in that their fangs are set well back in the jaw and, because of that, they are supposed to be unable to bite a person effectively.

The first time that we recovered the ROV there was a snake draped gracefully around the cable. That one gave no problems. It merely favoured us with a beady look and dropped back into the water, but late that night, when the off-shift crew were gathered to watch a tape of *Dances with Wolves* in the cinema, they recovered a less co-operative reptile. As soon as the technician approached the camera, not seeing the snake hidden behind it, the creature reared up about three feet, and bit him neatly in the hand. At that stage all hell broke loose.

The Tannoy crackled across the film soundtrack: 'Medic to the ROV shack, Code Blue.'

I was up and moving almost before I realised it. After a time you develop a sort of low-grade precognition for those calls. The ROV shack was dark and lit with blood-red bulbs to improve the night vision of the men who spend a twelve-hour shift watching a TV monitor. The tech who had been bitten was pale under the sick looking light. His boss was a tough Geordie called Sammy. He was not the most popular man aboard.

Sammy said, 'Shit-for-brains here has got a bite.'

'What bit you?' I asked, ignoring the tension in the shack. Everyone on board knew that these two did not work together well and Gerry had already said openly that one or the other of them would have to go.

Sammy said, 'A snake for Christ's sake. Who else could get bitten by a sea snake?'

I said, 'OK, let's get you upstairs. Can you walk?'

'Yes.'

It was the first word the casualty had got in so far.

Sammy said, 'Don't be all fucking night.'

He wasn't my favourite person either so I said, 'I'll be as long as it takes.'

'Always the same, you Band Aid lot.'

I ignored him and concentrated on the injured man. As far as I could tell under that light, he was pale, clammy, and shocked. But there had hardly been time yet for the venom to work.

Under the hospital lights it was clear that he was indeed shocked, and that in turn was going to be a problem. Sea snakes are Elapids and their venom is neurotoxic, interfering with nerve conduction and causing doubling of vision and shallow respiration. Eventually it kills by switching off the nerves controlling breathing.

The problem is of course that the early symptoms of poisoning are the same as the symptoms of shock. I took his pulse, one hundred and thirty and thready. The punctures were tiny, spaced about an inch apart and blanched around the wounds as if two pins had been thrust in there. The blanching might be something, or again it might not. Snake venom is said to dilate the pupils but his eyes looked fine.

I took the single pack of polyvalent antivenom out of the fridge and read through the leaflet that was taped to it. It was not encouraging. 'Prepare to treat idiosyncratic reactions to animal serum. Maintain IV line. Prepare adrenalin injection in case of Anaphylaxis. This product can have serious or fatal side effects if misused.' Worst of all was the casual instruction 'Titrate against symptoms.'

In other words this stuff was highly dangerous to administer and there was no clear dose rate. You simply gave it until the patient was better and then stopped. If, that is, the patient survived the experience. I took out an IV cannula and stood up a vein on his left arm. For a mercy the Venflon went in cleanly. All the time he lay there looking sick.

He said, 'Is it bad?'

'No. The IV line is just in case. If you do react to the bite I want to be able to dose you easily, and it's the best route.'

'I'm not going to die am I?'

'God no. Look. We have the antivenom here.'

I showed him the pack. As I did so I saw a note that a previous medic had appended to the instructions in Biro. 'K.Y.A.G.' it said in blue ink. Industry standard for, 'Kiss Your Arse Goodbye.'

He said, 'Can't I have the stuff right away? In case like.'

'No, it doesn't work that way. I don't want to shoot you full of this stuff if I don't have to.'

'How long before we know?'

I glanced at my watch. It had been maybe ten minutes since the bite.

'Three-quarters of an hour or so.'

'How will I know?'

'If you've been poisoned you'll know.'

I had to avoid telling him the symptoms in his highly suggestible state.

'I feel cold.'

'That's OK. You're a little shocked that's all. Did it give you a fright?'

'Christ, mate, did it ever.'

He related the incident with relish and, with the thought of how good it would sound in the bar later, the worst of the shock subsided. This too complicated things, because a false euphoria is also associated with neuro venoms.

He was more relaxed. I wasn't. I kept looking back to the inscription on the antivenom. KYAG indeed!

The time dragged past. Nothing developed. After three-quarters of an hour I was more or less certain there would be no reactions but I gave it twenty minutes more to be sure and then pulled the IV line and plastered over the puncture. The patient was elated.

'Why didn't it poison me? After all it did bite.'

'Probably out of venom. It happens a lot when they are hunting. Incidentally what did you do with the snake?'

'Do? Nothing. It's still there.'

'What? Jesus H. Christ.'

I ran for the steps to the ROV shack, leaving the man sitting there looking after me as if I had gone insane. But by the time I was halfway down the steps I could see it was too late.

Sammy was climbing the steps towards me holding his left hand in his right. In his agitation his Geordie accent was almost unintelligible.

'I got bit. Bit, d'ye hear?'

Indeed. By a snake whose venom sacs were exhausted.

'I got fucking bit. Are ye no' going to treat it?'

'Sure, come in.'

'God, man, I need help.'

'OK, take your shirt off and lie down there.'

'How bad is it?'

'Hard to tell. If you're still drawing breath in an hour or two you'll probably be OK.'

'You mean I might die?'

'I don't believe in lying to a man who's in danger of his life. Yes, you might. But I don't think that you will.'

'Can you no' do something? A tourniquet and cut the wound open?'

'And suck out the poison I suppose? You read too many paperback Westerns. All that does is spread the venom and leave me a stitching job on top of the snakebite.'

I stood up a vein on his forearm and slipped a Venflon into place, taped the cannula and sealed it with a plastic cap. Really at that point the fun had gone on long enough. I looked at the wounds on his hand. Identical punctures, identical snake, no venom.

'I don't think there's venom in this wound in any case.'

'You can tell by looking?'

'Sure. If you know what to look for.'

We waited the statutory hour and afterwards I took the cannula out and plastered the puncture over.

Later, in the galley I overheard him.

'And you know yon medic he could tell just by looking, man. He's a canny man to have looking after you when you'se sick.'

After a build-up like that it would have been a shame to disillusion him. Gerry, who was very well aware of the real state of affairs, was less impressed.

'I've never met a medic yet who wasn't a bloody con man,' he said. 'In the best possible way of course.'

I felt that I had to take that as a compliment.

*   *   *

By the end of the first two surveys we were starting to think that the whole job, including its massively inflated bonus payments, was overrated.

We had combed two platforms, from the splash zone to the seabed, and turned up nothing more lethal than a loose anticorrosion electrode. Of the fabled munitions there had, as yet, been no sign.

Years before, in laboratory work that involved the endless repetition of a complex operation, I had encountered expectation fatigue. Finding nothing for days on end eventually blunts your perceptions. In a lab, of course, the management can slip in a few known positive results to encourage you a little, but no such manipulation was possible here, and by the time we set up near the third platform we were all far too relaxed to work well.

The ROV spotted it first on the eighty-foot level. The camera had been nosing around, hour after hour, examining the endless cross bracings of the underwater steelwork and finding nothing, until finally, an object swam into view on the monitor.

It was a long, drab-coloured cylinder, with a bundle of wires running from it to a largish watertight box. It could have been anything. Often the steelwork has odd exotic monitoring equipment for stress and strain measurements, but this was held to the steel by a series of rough metal strappings that were obviously recent as they still shone in the lights.

The alert went out over the Tannoy right away. If this was a bomb it was well placed. The steel member that it was strapped to held the main clamp for the marine risers carrying oil and gas from the wells beneath. An explosion there would sever all of them and cause an instant and very deadly fireball.

The clearance divers gathered in the cinema to examine the video tape of the thing.

'Russian Mk 6?' offered one man.

'No. It's too bloody short and in any case what the hell is in that box?'

Gerry, who, as dive superintendent, was in overall charge of operations, called them to order.

'Well,' he said, 'you've all seen it and I think it's safe to say that no one recognises it. It could be a home-cooked device that the local commander brewed up, or it might be something else entirely. We have to assume that it is a bomb and that it is active. I've no real thoughts on fuses, besides what most of you will have thought of already, but I'm going to go through them in case it sparks some ideas.

'It could have a proximity device, either acoustic or photocell. I think we could rule out magnetic fuses because of the steel of the platform. It might have a timer. They run up to a year if need be, and, of course, it might simply be rigged on a tilt switch so if we poke it it goes off. Best best is that the control and fuse system is in the box with a simple detonator in the main charge, if that's what that cylinder thing is.

'I suggest that we try to isolate one from the other. That control cable bundle between the two looks vulnerable so we'll dissect that to start with. Of course cutting into that might be a problem in itself, so whoever starts is going to have to go in very slow and easy. The ROV will watch each move as usual. Right, let's go to work.'

He didn't mention, didn't have to mention, that the point about the ROV watching was that if the device should explode, we would have a record, so that the next man to try to make one of these safe would have something to go on.

It was very shallow, only an air dive, so I was delegated to watch on deck and keep the hospital ready in case of need. Not that, if an underwater explosion took place, the diver would be in need of anything but one of the large PVC body bags, tucked discreetly away in the cupboard where only I would have to know they were there.

Billy, as senior ordnance expert, was diver one, and, as he was dressing, just before we clamped the hot water hose to his suit he said, 'Jon, if anything happens there's an envelope in my cabin. Can you make sure it gets posted?'

'Yes, of course, mate. And for Christ's sake be careful.'

'Don't worry. I'll keep you out of a job.'

We dropped the helmet on to the neck dam around his shoulders and latched it tight. From then on he could only talk to the supervisor in dive control. But his eyes said it all. Hyped up, so tight wired that he seemed ready to jump at a pin drop, he had the look of a man who was doing what he knew best, and doing it superbly well. In fact he was enjoying himself.

The ROV picked up his lights before we could make out his form in the slightly clouded water at the eighty-foot level. Presently he materialised out of the murk and gave a thumbs up to the camera. All over the ship, all the available monitors were tuned to his channel. Very few of the off watch crew were below in the accommodation. I suppose that the thought of sleeping below the waterline with a live mine in close proximity had spoiled their rest.

Billy sat astride the member as if riding a horse. The control cable ran away from him and the box that we assumed was the control system was directly in front of him, almost in his lap. His voice was distorted, and bubbles rattled in the regulator, but we could understand clearly enough.

He said, 'The cable bundle looks like a home-made job. There are quite a few wires in there but there doesn't seem to be an antihandling mesh over them so I reckon it's safe to cut into it to expose the wires.'

He was worried that the soft sheathing was hiding a copper mesh like that around a TV coaxial aerial. If it was, cutting into it would disturb a protective field charge through the mesh, trigger a cascade amplifier, and pulse the detonator. We all waited, tensely, as he slit into the sheath with a bronze cutter. There was no bubbling in the regulator now and I realised that Billy was holding his breath.

He said, 'OK. I'm through the sheath. If this is a bomb it's a dead crude fucker. All the wires in here look like 5 amp marine cable. It's all single core and it's all pink. There's no colour coding at all. I suppose that was too much to hope for. I'll try and pick up the lives with a field meter.'

He touched each cable in turn with a device that would register the tiny trickle current that protected a normally closed loop from interference. Once again cutting the wrong loop could be a fatal error.

'No, nothing. Except. Wait a minute. The top two wires are the field loop. There's no way of telling them from the others as far as I can see, but they definitely have a field current.

'That's bloody awkward. If they are just antihandling dummies that's OK, but if they feed the detonators as well it's going to be tough to cut the buggers out. Still it's a crude bugger. OK, topside. This is what I'm going to do. I shall cut each wire in turn leaving the antihandling loop intact. If I'm right about the way this is wired, that will leave just the loop and isolate the main detonator off. After that I can cut the det wires and that should be it. After all, if there's no circuit the sodding thing can't go bang, can it?'

He paused and for a time all we could hear was his breathing.

Then he said, 'After that we'll recover the box to the surface and try to work out if we can move the main charge.'

He took a pair of cutters and, as each wire parted, the ship stood still waiting for the bang that never came. Finally he said, 'Got you, you bastard.' And, taking the now isolated box, he carried it back to the personnel basket for recovery.

When he was safely sealed into the deck chamber for his decompression the box was isolated in the middle of a large bare area of deck. The idea now was to examine it in detail and, we hoped, gain enough insight into the working of the trigger to decide on how to move the much more lethal main charge.

The man who was landed with this job was Tom Jackson, the electronics specialist, such a very quiet soul he seemed almost withdrawn. I hardly knew him. Yet approaching the job was the only time I had seen him look completely relaxed.

He unrolled a toolkit beside the box, gave the outer case a cursory examination and started in on the Allen bolts that held the lid on. One by one he removed them, placing each neatly on the deck beside him, and finally he took off the lid.

As he did so he lost a deal of his apparent composure. He put the box very gently down on the deck and snipped delicately at a pair of wires. A second later he placed a slim aluminium cylinder about three inches long on the deck, well away from the dismantled box. The object was a detonator.

'Nasty-minded bastards,' he said, 'booby-trapped the bloody box. The switch must have jammed. Either that or the battery hasn't got the push to fire the bugger. Still, we'd be better off without this.'

He took out a wodge of greyish putty and put it down gently. It was a small charge of military plastic.

'Not much of it but it would still spoil your day,' he called cheerfully.

'Right. It's a standard timer and radio fuse system. It's been modified a bit to fire from a surface command cable. This socket here' – he pointed briefly – 'is where it could be plugged in. I wonder why they didn't fire it? It's really just a standard demolition charge fuse. Well, lads, I reckon we can relax.'

He put the box down, sat back and lit a cigarette. The tension relaxed visibly. Presently he said, 'I'll take this baby down to the workshop and pull it apart. We might find out something more.'

With the departure of the box everyone relaxed. The plastic explosive and detonator were dispatched overboard. Billy, fresh from decompression, was wearing a huge grin and a towel and enjoying the sunshine.

Having come so far we felt happy and confident. The feeling lasted right up until the door of the workshop flew open to the sharp crack of an explosion.

In emergencies time is elastic. I suppose that the real elapsed time, from the moment that the explosion turned every head on the deck towards the workshop door, to the moment when two of us stood at the doorway itself, looking through a cloud of bluish smoke that smelled of fireworks, was only a few seconds.

It seemed like hours. It seemed that we could not move quickly enough. That the world was swimming by in slow motion, cased under a clear layer of crystal. And then the doorway was in front of us, and the workshop was there, looking much as it always had, and there, lying on the floor, crumpled into a corner, was Tom the technician.

His Kevlar body armour had taken the worst of the blast and it could, in any case, have only been a tiny charge, but in that confined space it was enough. His right hand was throw carelessly open on the deck plates. Three fingers were missing. He must have had that hand on the box when the charge burst. There was very little bleeding. No squirting arterial jets marked the amputated stumps. I knew even before I touched him that the reason was that his heart had stopped.

I turned him gently on to his back. Aside from the hand and the whitish flash burn to the body armour there was no other mark of violence on his body.

Billy was standing beside me, looking down expectantly. He said, 'How bad is it, mate?'

There's no easy way to pronounce death, not ever. So I just said it.

'He's dead.'

'Can't you get him going again?'

'Billy, he's smashed up inside.'

'But he looks OK.'

'Yes, I know that, but his lungs are burst. There's nothing more to do for him.'

'Christ. He thought it was clear.'

'Well, we all did.'

'I worked with him before, you know. He was going to be married. He only came on this job to get the money to give them a start.'

'There was a second charge in the control box. We'd best radio the beach and tell them. There'll be an inquiry. We should leave the body where it is.'

Gerry was behind him in the doorway. He shook his head.

'Not this time. He isn't officially here. You'd better bag him up and sort out his effects.'

'We can't just ship him home without a legal inquiry.'

'There's no law here to inquire. Look Jon, there's thousands of bodies lying in the desert only a few miles up-country. Do you think that they'll bother with one more?'

'But this wasn't a war.'

'Now who the bloody hell gave you a stupid idea like that?'

We bagged him as gently as we could, enclosing him in the last dark night of the polythene cocoon and zipping him up. We took the Kevlar body armour off first though. It was as Gerry had said. This was an undeclared casualty, in an undeclared war, and there was nothing left to do but send the body home.

*   *   *

It was a full two weeks searching after that before we found our next mine. During that time we had minutely searched three sets of steel structures and found nothing of significance. Nothing explosive that is. Even after so long in the industry, I am still amazed by the things that people manage to lose overboard.

During those intervening two weeks we found three fork-lift trucks, a smashed and useless ship's lifeboat, two heavy-duty drill bits, and drilling pipe and scaffolding tube beyond all measure. This is of course a secondary problem in mine-clearance. Amongst such a heap of tangled junk, there are hundreds of objects that, seen in the half-lit murk of the sea floor, could be potential bombs.

About the second find however there was no doubt at all. It was floating, anchored to a steel cable, three feet below the surface, inside the structure of a platform. How it had been laid in such a difficult position, and why, was a mystery. The water being fairly clear we could see it from the surface. It was a steel sphere perhaps three feet across, nestled into a cradle of tubular steel members that extended beneath the sphere to form a base rather like a fancy plant stand. As always in real live mines, as opposed to practice ones, there were no markings of any kind on the casing. It was painted a uniform dull blue and it looked very businesslike and very lethal.

This was a situation that we had never envisaged. Because of where the mine was anchored it was surrounded on all sides by the steel work of the platform. At the nearest point it was twenty feet or so from the risers carrying oil to the surface, and while this particular well was cold, the subsea valves closed tight to halt the flow of oil and gas, an explosion at that point would destroy the production capacity of the platform for years to come.

To make things more difficult this was an area collection platform, collecting oil from a dozen satellites in the field and pumping it on. Blowing this one structure up would have a similar effect to the destruction of the *Piper Alpha*. It would simply close the entire field.

We stood in a row leaning over the side and looking at the mine. There was virtually no swell and it was slack water, so that the thrusters were holding us in position with almost no turbulence. The seeing was about as perfect as it could get.

Andy, our replacement tech, was knowledgeable about sea mines.

'That, folks, is a Russian Mk 7,' he said cheerfully.

'Or a Chinese copy,' put in Billy, who I think felt his own authority a little challenged.

'It's a bloody fine bit of engineering, mind,' said Andy in a placatory tone of voice.

'Yes. I just wish it would clear off and get itself admired somewhere else.'

'All kinds of fuses on them, you know.'

'Sure.'

'Can't blow it where it is.'

'No.'

'Can't tow it off either. It will hit the steelwork on the way out.'

'That's true.'

'So what the hell can we do?'

Billy was not in a forgiving mood and he simply said, 'God knows.'

'Lift it,' said Gerry in a bright voice.

Only old Billy was unfazed enough to ask, 'Lift it? Where to?'

'Well, if we put a cable on that padeye on the top of the charge and lift it with the crane boomed right out, we can cut the mooring cable under it easy enough. Then we can pull the ship off and bring the mine out on the end of the crane and drop it in the ocean to blow it.'

'For God's sake,' said Billy, scandalised by the risks inherent in that idea, 'are you serious?'

'Well, what could go wrong? At the worst we'll lose the crane hook.'

'What about the shrapnel?'

'Keep everyone under cover during the lift.'

'Who's going to drive the crane?'

'I will.'

We all looked at him. Up until then we had been unaware that a suicidal maniac had been running the job.

Billy said, 'You must be kidding.'

But he wasn't.

Actually it was so simple that it was almost farcical. We put a line on to the padeye, cut the cable and lifted the mine clear of the water leaving it dangling like a big conker on the end of its string. The ship pulled off and the crane boom moved gracefully out of the steelwork. Perhaps it was because it had been so very easy up until then that Gerry made his first mistake.

Crane driving looks easy. In fact it looks so easy that we all have had a go at it at one time or another, usually to shift something that won't matter too much if we bash it about a bit. But cranes are very odd machines indeed.

Because the boom of the crane can go up and down as well as the cable moving, the driver has to co-ordinate movements very carefully. Lifting the boom up without paying out cable lifts the load towards the pulley on the end of the crane. To stop enthusiastic drivers trying to pull the crane hook through the pulley altogether there is a limiter on the wire that switches off the power when the hook gets to within ten feet or so of the end of the boom. I think that it was that limiter switch that tripped at that point, leaving the mine suspended from the end of the crane wire, about thirty feet directly above the deck.

And there it stayed. Despite all our attempts to free the wire and coax the reluctant crane back into action, there it stayed.

You can, it seems, get used to just about anything. Even 500 kilos of high explosives dangling above you like a technological sword of Damocles. Of course, to complicate matters further, events of this nature, once they get going, develop a momentum of their own.

The crane, despite our very best efforts and the efforts of all of the ship's engineers, remained steadfastly immobile. In the end they decided that the only way to free off the limiter was to release the wire manually, lower the mine to the deck, very gently, and thus to release the tension on the crane. We were not enamoured of this procedure. Of course the objections were not logical. The mine had already allowed itself to be picked up, moved out of the water and swung about on the end of a crane hook, and it seemed more than likely that it would prove equally docile when rested gently on the deck, but logic loses much of its force in such situations.

The actual lowering was carried out just at sunset. It made a fine dramatic picture with the crane silhouetted against a sky the colour of arterial blood. There was by that stage a patrol vessel of the Royal Saudi Navy standing by, but we couldn't help noticing that, as the actual lowering operation started, their stand-by position seemed a few hundred yards more distant than before.

Eventually the suspended mine was within touching distance of the deck. Usually whenever a load is moving, those on deck give a hand to seeing it into position so it sits neatly where we want it. The mine was allowed to find its own deck space.

After an hour or so curiosity had overcome fear to the point where small groups wandered up to the mine to walk around it. At close quarters it looked even more evil than when it had been in the water, but it was because of this close inspection that someone noticed a faint but definite hiss from the complex mass of control gear below the spherical explosive charge.

Billy came back on the run.

'Jesus,' he said, 'the bugger's doing something.'

The men who had been near it melted away like smoke in a high wind. Deck radios were inoperative because of the risk of setting off one of the electronic fuses, and because of that, someone had to run to the nearest deck telephone point to acquaint the bridge with the situation.

The Saudi gunboat swung towards us, her bows throwing two wings of phosphorescence as she came.

Billy was still next to the mine. From my own position, as far down the deck as I could get, I saw him reach down and poke at something. He looked closely at it for a moment then strolled to the side, leaned

over and lit a smoke. The Saudi gunboat hove to beside us in a flurry
of foam and threw us a line. The crew divided into two groups. Some
were frantically heading for the rail, ready to leap the three-foot gap
to the other vessel. Others were looking at Billy, who continued to
smoke his smoke and lean. Presently someone summoned up the
courage to go up to him, then he waved to me to come over.

'Well?' I said, mindful of the hissing mine only feet away.

'Friend of yours,' said Billy, gesturing towards the mine.

'Friend? How do you mean?'

'Look at the bottom, in the base where there's a pool of sea water,
and don't stick your fingers in.'

I looked. A large sea snake was coiled there, hissing like a
tea kettle.

'That was it?'

'Sure. Tell the crew they can come out now.'

'But you let them jump over to the gunboat.'

'Yes. On jobs like this, mate, it's good to know who'll bottle
out.'

We dropped the mine over the side the next day and ran a heavy
charge of gelatine and a radio detonator on to it. The explosion,
when it finally came, was, as they say, worth waiting for. It was
very shallow of course, but even so the sight was impressive. About
a half square mile of sea tensed itself and threw up a huge white
foam geyser into the limpid air of the morning. It felt as if a great
hot hand had shoved gently at the ship and the sound was so abrupt
and guttural that it was gone almost before there was time to register
it properly.

Eventually the sea settled itself back into order and there was
nothing to show for the incident save a few dead fish and the
sharks, attracted as always by the explosion, cruising aimlessly back
and forth through the water.

* * *

For three more weeks we searched the water for mines but apart
from a single find of a Second World War bomb, dropped God
knows how long ago in some long-forgotten action, there were no
more incidents.

Eventually, six weeks of that sort of activity being as long as a crew
is reckoned capable of standing, our tour of duty in the Gulf came to
an uneventful end. We were to spend a night in the imposing tower
of the Kuwait Plaza Hotel on our way out of the country. Already,

so soon after the war, the work of reconstruction was well underway. Where the streets had been full of UN task force soldiers there were now construction workers of all nationalities. All around the hotel the buildings were covered in scaffolding and the night was busy with the rumble of heavy diesels.

Gerry came to my room late on that night. He plonked himself down in a chair and took out a long white envelope.

'Bit early for your paycheque to come through,' I said.

'When you get home, Jon, will you give this to Sue for me?'

There had been warning signs enough so I didn't pretend that I was surprised.

I said, 'I don't want to interfere, mate, but you are sure?'

'Yeah. Tell her, tell her that it's for the best, Jon.'

'I'll tell her, Gerry, but she won't believe me.'

'Maybe she will.'

'How long have you been together?'

'Eighteen years.'

'God almighty, Gerry. What will you do?'

'Stay on here. After all, there's work available and if I'm going to make a fresh start I'll need the money.'

'Is there anything else that you want me to tell her?'

'No.'

'How about the kids?'

'They are old enough to understand.'

'All right, mate. Good luck wherever it takes you.'

'Yes. You too. Keep 'em alive, Jon.'

He reached into a plastic bag that I hadn't seen before that moment. It held a bottle of rye.

'I couldn't go without saying goodbye properly,' he said, pouring into two toothglasses.

'Where did that come from?' I asked. Kuwait is a Muslim country.

'One of the Yanks. Don't even ask what it cost.'

We sat for a time in silence with the sounds of the rebuilding coming in through the double-glazing.

Finally he said, 'I'll see you before you fly in the morning.'

'Sure, I'll come looking if you don't.'

I looked for him that morning, but he was already gone and it was a whole year and a lot of water under the bridge before I saw Gerry again.

11

In Miri, the oil base tucked away on the west coast of Sarawak, it was the time of the Festival of the Hungry Ghosts among the Chinese community. Despite its fearsome-sounding name, this Taoist Festival of the Dead is a time of celebration when families visit the graves of their ancestors, cook food beside the memorials, and offer the returning ghosts a meal to warm them in the hereafter.

We were moored within a stone's throw of the Chinese graveyard whose boundaries came down to the water's edge, and from our upper deck we could watch the festivities as we worked to prepare the vessel to go to sea.

During the day there was little enough to see, but, as the darkness arrived with customary tropical suddenness, the daytime trickle of pilgrims became a flood and each small family group lit a charcoal cooking fire so that the graveyard resembled the campsite of a great army awaiting the morning to do battle.

Each night of the three days that it took us to ready the ship the ritual was repeated, and the thick, heavy scent of joss mixed with Chinese spices and the acrid nip of cooking charcoal would drift across to us from over the river and perfume the dusk.

As it happened we were due to sail on the final night of the week-long festival. That afternoon the telex had arrived. It always starts with the same traditional form of words from the owners' representatives, 'Being in all respects ready for sea dive ship *Eagle* will proceed from port on the next suitable tide.'

It is a form of words that always sends a thrill up the spine, part anticipation, part apprehension; we were going back to sea.

The tide was full at eleven at night and as we cast off our umbilical links with the land, a strange and rather wonderful thing happened.

All along the bank of the Chinese graveyard, where the land sloped down into the water, hundreds of people were carrying paper lanterns, lit from within by a flickering candle. They were all the pastel colours of nature in the early spring, and, as we pulled out into the current, the lanterns were set adrift and allowed to float free with the tide down the river.

Jimmy Chan, our Chinese cook, explained the spectacle to me from the open companionway door.

'It is the end of the festival. The ancestors must be shown the way back to the lands of the spirits for another year, they follow the lanterns away out to the sea.'

So, escorted by the ghosts of a thousand ancestors and surrounded by the pale lights of the lanterns' soft glowing, we slipped softly away down the river.

We were on a salvage job, the rough trade end of the industry where the rules that you work by are those that you make up as you go along and safety is, all too often, a long way down the priority list. Three weeks earlier the drilling rig *Al Hussein* had hit a pocket of gas while she was running a test well 120 miles east. The blow-out preventer either failed or was never fitted and the explosion wiped out the rig, leaving her in 200 feet of water, on top of a series of very expensive holes in the seabed. We were off to clear the debris. The locals wanted the wreckage off those wells. If we could help ourselves to some useful salvage while we were about it, that was a bonus. A good salvage job, where the ship raises all the expensive units off a wreck, might be worth as much as twenty thousand pounds to every man aboard on top of the usual day rate. It promised to be an interesting job.

It had interested Billy Carson, too. His lined and battered face seemed to haunt my working life but by now he was a friend.

'I hear Gerry finally decided to call it a day,' he remarked as we stood on deck watching our progress down river.

'Sort of. He sent me home with a letter for Sue.'

'She's better off without him. He should never have married.'

'I thought they were happy.'

'You know how it is with him. The job first and last. Sue probably got tired of being second in line.'

'I thought you felt that way, too. After all, no one has more experience.'

'I did once, but things change. Or they get changed for you.'

'Good God, you are in a bad way.'

He grinned and turned away to look at the tip of the estuary where a sand bar reaches a finger of shoal out into the bay, a treacherous spot for the unwary, and many ships, attempting too rapid a turn, have been stranded if nothing worse. As we cleared the river, we could hear the shoal in the darkness, a rumble of white water breaking on the shallows. The Chinese lanterns, those few that were left, tilted, were swamped, and overturned, until finally the last small brave light was lost in the surf and the ship turned gently outwards towards the empty quiet waters of the South China Sea.

* * *

Morning found us out of sight of land, though a few of the thousands of islands that make up Malaysia humped blue into the sky where the horizon line bounded our vision. These waters are still infested by river pirates, and, while a diving ship is not really much of a prize, the risk was sufficiently real to force us to keep a lookout on all small vessels within our radar range.

Modern piracy can be every bit as brutal as its sixteenth-century counterpart, and the technique is simple. Typically the victim is one of the huge bulk carriers that sail for hundreds of miles on preset courses, often with minimal radio and radar watches. The pirate ship, usually a small junk with a long-tailed V8 engine, slips quietly under the stern of the larger vessel at night. From there on, boarding is as simple as throwing a grappling iron over the rail, and climbing the hanging eighty feet or so of knotted rope. Once aboard, the armed men hold the bridge watch at gunpoint, force the captain to open his safe, and then leave with the ship's ready cash, often a matter of twenty thousand sterling or so in currency.

Occasionally the ship itself, and the millions of dollars' worth of cargo, have been the target, and in such cases the crew are simply disposed of overboard and the vessel reappears in the crowded harbours of the Far East, often with a name change, false papers, and false bills of lading, that effectively cover the crime.

Because of this we were extremely nervous of the apparently helpless junk that we sighted about twenty hours out of Miri, drifting in a listless fashion before a slight breeze.

As we edged closer, we could make out people hung over the splintered rails, and lying on the deck in attitudes that suggested the late stages of sea sickness. There were not only men, but women and children. The whole junk had the appearance of an overcrowded floating refugee camp, and that, in effect, was what it was.

'Boat people,' said Tony the skipper, as we edged closer to the vessel. 'North Vietnamese by the look of them. Do you care to go aboard? They always need a medic.'

'Sure, but what then? Do we tow them in?'

'Shit no. No one will accept them officially. Malaysia sends them back if they are lucky, or turns them back out to sea if the local official is feeling pissed off. Hong Kong interns them. The Philippines don't want them. Taking them on is more trouble than we can afford, old mate.'

'So we just leave them?'

'No. First we give them water and food, and medical attention if you are willing. Then we tell them where they are, and point them in the direction of land, and *then* we leave them.'

There was no point in arguing. In any case he was right. We could only do the best we could and pass on. There was a chance, if they were very lucky, that one of the American patrols might pick them up and offer a chance of resettlement.

Close to, the junk stank of tight-packed humanity and excrement. I suppose that it was the same smell that the slavers had about them in the bad old days. But her decks were scrubbed white and bleached by the sun, and the clothes that the people wore were clean and fresh washed.

Apart from one ancient man whose face seemed to be mainly two black marmoset eyes gazing out of a nest of wrinkles, and who had a clean simple fracture of the wrist, there were no serious illnesses on board.

I set up the green striped can of plaster bandages on the deck where the sun gave me light enough to see properly.

The rules were strict in such cases. None of the refugees was to board the ship except in the event of a sinking. I had heard stories around the bars back in Miri of desperate boat people, who, knowing the rules, had sunk their own craft in sight of nearby shipping, in order to be taken aboard. There were dark rumours too that even in such circumstances there were skippers who simply sailed away.

The old man tolerated my attentions with a stolidity that was amazing, equally accepting even the bone grinding wrench that reduced the fracture to a fair semblance of normality, and that would have had a Westerner yelling in pain.

Watched by a whole gathering of small children, I wrapped the limb, plastered it, and, with the help of a youngish woman, who could speak a few words of English, gave instructions on aftercare.

As for the rest of the people, they were healthy enough, considering that they had been three weeks at sea, under rough conditions, in a vessel that would hardly have been thought fit to have safely crossed the harbour back home.

The skipper of this floating marine junk heap explained, in mixed English, Pidgin, Tagalog, and gestures, that they were two weeks out of Vietnam when the engine had quit. Since then they had sighted ships but no one had stopped.

Our second engineer struggled for a time with the ancient Leyland bus engine that drove the thing, and in the end, after an hour or so, there was a plume of stinking blue smoke and a choppy roar of power and they were once again free to carry on their journey to nowhere.

They lined the deck to watch us as they pulled away, young women in black pyjamas and conical sunhats, men, old crones, kids with grave oriental faces and in the middle of them, the old man, proudly displaying his pristine white plaster cast and grinning with his toothless mouth.

*   *   *

With the refugee craft no more than a receding dot on the ocean I went below to the galley in search of company. One might think that, on a 200-foot vessel, space being at a premium, solitude would be harder to find than fellow humans, but, in fact, often the opposite is true, especially when the ship is not actually working.

Working ships have order and pattern. There are people everywhere, carrying out some essential function or other. Ships on downtime are different. No one is keen on being observed to do nothing on shift and so, rather than be so observed, people hide and that is why I was heading for the galley looking for company.

As usual there was a small knot of men gathered around the coffee machine, drinking the fierce Norwegian brew that seems to have infested just about every diving vessel in the world. Its one major advantage is that, though it might be very near undrinkable, a couple of mugs of it will keep you awake, even during the most tedious of dog-watches.

I got to talking with Jack Darling, a tough Aussie diver whose usual stamping ground was the waters of the Arabian Gulf, but who had been attracted to this job by the prospect of salvage experience.

He was a man who truly looked the part. Two fingers were missing on his left hand. His skin was burned the colour of old oak and he had arms that swelled with muscle and jutted away from his shoulders when he moved. There were those aboard who swore that Jack walked on his knuckles when he came up a gangway, but I had attended a casualty with him as my only help a few years back, and, despite his fearsome appearance, he was caring and compassionate. Also he was worried and that was a bad sign in a man who did not let life's little problems get to him easily.

He said, 'Look, mate, can I ask you something? On the quiet like?'

'Of course,' I said. Usually, when a man starts out that way it means he has, or thinks he has, a medical condition that he feels embarrassed about, so it's an approach I get to hear quite often.

This time though it was different. Instead of a red-faced enquiry about piles or something equally undignified he said, 'If a bloke was taking heavy drugs, you'd know about it wouldn't you?'

'Well, that depends on if it was a prescribed medication. If it was legal, well, in theory, I'd get word from the beach. Of course, if it was backstreet. Well, that's another thing again.'

'No, mate. It's not Crack or nothing like it. It's just that, well, look, what's Cyclomorph used for?'

'Well, you're damn right it's heavy. It's a mixture of morphine with an anti-nausea compound. It's used to control severe pain. It's serious stuff. Whenever we use it we have to refer back to the beach for a doctor's approval.'

'So. What if it was bought illegally here in Malaysia?'

'Christ, don't even think about it. They hang you for possession of more than five grams of Opium equivalent here.'

'So I reckon we'd be talking heavy shit. Right, mate?'

'Very heavy indeed.'

He said nothing else, so I waited a few minutes, and, as he just sat there sipping his coffee, I said, 'Jack, if you know someone who is using that stuff, they need help, mate. Now I'm not asking you to betray a confidence but I should know. I mean a man with that kind of habit needs to be in a position where he can't hurt anyone else.'

'You mean that he'd get run off?'

'No, maybe not. By rights he would of course, but if we can't look after our own, who the hell else will?'

'OK, mate. Thanks for the advice.'

'Sure. And Jack, please tell him to talk to me.'

So much for company. I went looking for a peaceful coffee and a chat about old friends and got told that one of the crew was using heavy dope. It was not a comforting idea to think of a man that troubled somewhere among the crew.

The oilfields of the Malaysian waters are relatively young, so there are few platforms in each field. In fact the wreck that we were seeking to demolish was only an isolated dot of man-made wreckage in a great open undersea plain patrolled only by the Mantas and the cruising predatory sharks.

Finding a wreck at sea sounds very complex, and years ago, when open-water navigation was less a science than a fine art, it must have been. However, we knew with great precision where the wreck lay, and, with the aid of triple satellite fixes, we were on station above the derelict forty-eight hours after leaving Miri.

For the first three days or so our schedule called for the ROV to carry out a deep sea survey. Divers look on this swimming TV camera with a mixture of mistrust and sheer dislike. After all, in a few years, many of the lucrative inspection programmes will fall to the ROV but for the first vital survey work it remains essential.

The pictures that it sent back to the ship were relayed all over the vessel by closed circuit cable, and the view was not encouraging. Two hundred and fifty feet below us the seabed looked like a scrapyard. The rig, in its collapse, had fallen sideways, buckling the massive steel lattices of its legs so that the main deck, a steel platform some three hundred feet square and weighing over eight hundred tonnes, was balanced at an angle of some forty degrees or so, supported by a rough triangle of smashed and distorted steel tracery that was like a massive subsea adventure playground designed for giants.

To the east, in the direction of fall, were the remains of the drilling tower and a littered jumble of hundreds of steel drill string tubes, half tonne jack straws in a big heap on the bottom. To complicate matters further, the whole picture of the site was not comprehensible from any one angle. Underwater visibility is rarely more than a few hundred feet at best, and the wreck site, spread out as it was over a half square mile, could only be photographed in parts and a matrix created of the whole.

It was during the survey phase that Jack called me to one side again. His almost comically ugly face was set in an expression of concern, and he had an air of urgency.

'About the other day,' he said.

'Right. Is the guy ready to talk?'

'No. But it's getting worse. You'll have to know sooner or later. Look, old Billy, you two know each other, right?'

'Yes. We go back a way. What is he to do with anything?'

'Well, maybe I should just butt out. No probs.'

'Hey, wait a minute. If you have something you think I ought to know about Billy, then for God's sake go ahead and tell me.'

'Well, it's difficult with him being a mate of yours.'

'Just tell me, OK? I'll say nothing outside these walls.'

'Well. He's the one with the problem,'

'Billy? No. No way. Look, even in West Africa when they all blew a little grass he wouldn't go that route. He likes a drink now and then, but that's all.'

'Christ, this is more difficult than I thought.'

'OK. You think he's using, right? What makes you think that?'

He reached into the pocket of his boiler suit and brought out a foil blister wrap of white tablets. The yellow band across the pack read 'Cyclomorph, to be dispensed only on the orders of a registered medical practitioner.'

'You sure that he's actually taking these?'

'Too right. Morning and night he slips a couple down when he thinks I'm not watching. Normally I'd say that if a man wants to kill himself, then that's his right, but he's supervising out here, man. We can't risk him being out of his head on the panel.'

'No, you're right of course. Look, will you leave it with me for now? I'll try to sort something out. You did right to come to me. I promise it'll not just rest. I'll do something about it.'

He left having passed on the responsibility. A dive boss who was stoned was a terrible hazard to us all, but this was no abstract case. I owed Billy Carson a lot.

In the end I cornered him in his cabin a few hours later. I put the foil wrap on the bed in front of him and said, 'We need to talk.'

For a moment I thought that he was going either to cry or hit me, but then it passed and he said, 'I suppose it was Jack?'

'Does it matter who? They are yours, aren't they?'

'Yes.'

'But why? You don't need that sort of shit.'

'I thought that you were a better medic than to need to ask that.'

It is strange how the obvious will be in front of your nose for days and yet remain hidden. In the tiny cabin the lights were hard white fluorescent, and they picked up every wrinkle and crease in a man's face. There were lines there that I had not seen before, lines that I was fairly sure had not been there a few weeks ago. I looked at his chest movement and the signs were there to read as clear as day. The right side was sluggish and hardly moved on inspiration. I had no stethoscope with me, but I knew that if I had listened to the breath sounds, there would have been silence on that side. In a man of over sixty, with a long history of smoking home rolls, and the weight loss that had caused the new wrinkles, there was only one realistic possibility. I said, 'How long?'

'You mean how long have I known? A long time. You know, you get used to it. There are even some advantages. At least I shall never grow old to bore my relatives' kids around the fire. It's not so bad. After all, who needs old age? I never did see myself as a snoring, farting, fat old man.'

'It's inoperable of course?'

'Shit, yes. Both lungs, liver, colon, the whole bloody shooting match.'

'How long have you got?'

'If I'm good and I stay off cigs, don't drink, and eat well, six months or less.'

He lit another home roll, puffed blue smoke into the air and said, 'I reckon maybe three.'

'Jesus. I'm so sorry, man.'

'Yes. I know you are. Look, do me one last favour, mate?'

'Anything.'

'Right. Say fuck all. Let me finish my trip. It'll be the last after all and then, at the end, we'll have a run ashore in Miri. After that, well, I suppose I'll go back to India.'

'India?'

'Yes. There was a girl once, a long time ago. Well, she'd be middle-aged by now but she taught me a few things about the way that they look at dying. I want to be there in the end.'

I remembered my own first visit to India, with Gerry in happier times, and our visiting the Fire Temple where you could see the future in the flames, and I recognised that could indeed be a place for a man, alone in the world, to choose to make his peace with the infinite.

I wanted to say more but there was nothing left to say. Billy Carson had made all the decisions that needed making and he was already beyond my help, choosing his own accommodation with mortality.

* * *

As everyone knows, sailors have a reputation for romantic exploits in half the dubious bars in the known world. Years ago the inevitable, pitiful consequences of this trade were a very heavy load for the ship's doctor a few days afterwards. I can only speak from personal experience and, either times have changed, or sailors are more circumspect than they were wont to be. But on that trip there was one special case when it seemed that all the old stories were coming home to roost.

At the start of the trip we had no divers in saturation and my function at that point was to be medic and medic only. This is not quite so completely relaxing an assignment as it sounds. The hospital stocks of essentials quickly deteriorate in tropical heat and a constant updated inventory of the three hundred or so stock items is the only way of keeping a check on what needs reordering.

It was a lovely day, the sea was the colour of the sky but three shades darker, there was no swell other than the long lazy movements of the ocean rubbing itself against the keel under our feet. I was looking at this idyllic view in a rather vacant fashion when the knock came at the door.

Jai Khan, one of two brothers who were sailing with us for the first time, came in and stood uncertainly in the open space beside the couch that I use for examinations. He and his brother were part of the new breed of maritime gypsies, successors to the men who crewed the ocean tramps in the thirties. They often take long contracts and leave home for years at a time, mortgaging future earnings to fixers who are in turn paid by the shipping companies to hire cheap Third World crewmen. It is a lonely, achingly isolating way of life.

'What can I do for you, Jai?' I asked, after I had waited there in silence for a few minutes.

'Before I am telling you, it is important that you understand,' he said, rather confusingly.

'Understand what, mate?'

'They will say, the others, that I have been along River Street. But it is not true.'

Mention of Miri's notorious red-light district of course told me the likely nature of his predicament. But we are not on board to judge people, only to treat them, so I said, 'Jai. Whatever is the problem?'

'I am having a rash, sir.'

'Please don't call me "sir", mate. Now where is this rash?'

'Indeed, sir. It is most embarrassing.'

'Well, could I take a look at it?'

He slipped out of his boiler suit and stood in that awkward way that men have when naked in front of other men. There was a rash all right, pink and blotchy patches discoloured the golden bronze sheen of his skin. They extended in a rough band all around his genitals and thrust fingers down his upper thighs. It was like nothing I had ever seen or even heard of before. I felt for the regional lymph glands in his groin and of course they were swollen and tender, twin foci of infection.

'Do you have any pain?' I asked.

'Nothing at all, sir.'

'Does it hurt when you pass water?'

'Indeed not.'

I looked at the rest of him. Years ago doctors would call syphilis the 'Great Imitator' for its confusing presentations but this didn't even come close to any of those that I had read of. If it were syphilis the rash should be symmetrical, copper coloured and often on the arms. There was nothing else to help me, merely a few bruises on his upper torso, fading to dull purple. More to cover the fact that I was lost than to elicit information, I said, 'Did someone hit you?'

'Indeed they did not, sir,' he said in a tone that did not invite further enquiries.

I was surprised by the unexpectedly raw nerve, but let it pass and said, 'OK, OK, I was only joking. Look, I'll put you on a course of antibiotics. I'll start you with an injection and then we'll follow up by mouth for three days or so to clear it. You are being straight with me about the women?'

'Yes. Yes indeed, sir. There have been no women at all.'

I prepared a large intramuscular dose of long acting penicillin. This is the old stand-by in VD clinics the world over. Injected into a buttock it makes the patient non-infectious within hours and clears most common infections in a day or two.

As he was dressing he seemed more agitated than one might

expect even under such circumstances, and I said, 'Look, mate, it's just an illness. No one else knows.'

But he didn't seem in the mood for comforting and he left without another word.

Three days later he was back. The rash was no worse to be sure, but it was no better. There were still no other symptoms. This happens all too often enough in Asia, where the availability of antibiotics over the counter has led to their abuse over a period of years. The answer was simple. I switched antibiotic to tetracycline, and tried again.

By the end of the second course the rash was becoming a personal challenge. I pored through the ship's meagre medical library and tried to recall all that I had ever read of venereal infection but, after the whole of the second course, there it was, still bright pink, still not spreading, still inflaming the lymph glands, and still intractable.

'Jai,' I said, at last, after our third attempt, 'whatever this is, mate, it needs more specialised treatment than I can give. I'll have to get you back to the beach.'

He turned quite grey.

'Indeed not, sir. I cannot do this thing. I would rather suffer it than that.'

'All right, mate. I understand that. But I can't let an undiagnosed illness loose on the ship. It could be anything. No. I'm sorry. We'll have to get you back. But don't worry. I'll put it down as a medevac and you'll be on full pay the whole time.'

I left him sitting in the hospital while I went to make the arrangements, and, when I came back, Doran, Jai's brother, was waiting for me.

'Jai is most anxious, sir, to avoid being sent back,' he said.

'I know that,' I said, 'but it's not really up to me. He needs treatment.'

'Supposing that you were to know exactly how it was that he comes to have this rash. Could you treat him then yourself?'

'Well, it would surely help.'

'If I tell you, it will go no further?'

'No.'

'Very well. The night before we sailed we were drinking in the Sunset bar by the dock gate. You know it?'

'I know of it. But I thought that Jai said that there was no woman.'

'Just so. We were walking back to the ship and it must be said, sir, that we had had too much beer that night, when we saw, standing in the pathway in the moonlight, a very fine she-goat.'

'A goat?' I said, momentarily surprised out of detachment.

'Indeed yes.'

'And the rash was from the goat?'

'Yes.'

'And the bruises?'

'There was a fight over who was to enjoy the creature's favours.'

'And you lost?'

'Yes. May the Gods be praised.'

'Doran,' I said, ever alert for a wind-up, 'if you are taking the piss out of me, so help me you won't enjoy your next routine course of injections.'

'Sir. It is the simple truth.'

'A goat.'

There was a silence for a few minutes, then I said, 'Well, you had better send him back in.'

Understandably he was embarrassed. He shifted his weight all the time and had trouble meeting my eyes.

'Jai,' I said, 'you are going to have to take this treatment on faith, but I promise that it will probably work.'

I laid him on the examining table and painted the whole area of the rash with gentian violet tincture, colouring his whole lower body a rather fetching shade of lilac. Gentian is an old veterinary stand-by for skin infections.

'Now,' I said, 'leave it on. Don't wash it and keep it covered for twenty-four hours, then come back to see me.'

The next day the rash was gone.

Now a story so salacious is hard to keep quiet, and pretty soon, wherever the brothers went, divers bleated provocatively from all over the deck. Then it was forgotten, as most nine-day wonders are. It was months later, when I was in Miri again on another job, I was approached by an Aussie army medic who was researching local medicine.

'You must know a whole lot about this stuff by now, mate,' he said, encouraging me to share my knowledge of the mysterious East.

'Sadly no. It needs a system of belief that I really have no time for,' I said.

'Funny that,' he said, taking a pull at his drink and looking at me very directly over the foamed rim of the glass. 'I could have sworn that you were the bloke who cured a man of the clap by painting his dick purple.'

And to that dubious accolade I could find no suitable answer.

* * *

It was late on the first night of diving that we heard the firefight. We tracked shipping in the area as a matter of course, prudent navigation and the ever-present threat of piracy made sure of that, but no one had paid a lot of attention to the three converging green dots on the radar that represented three smallish craft just over our horizon.

We had heard enough gunfire before to recognise the sound, even without the arcing green tracers that broke the hazy line of the night sky and the sea. The shooting went on for some time, perhaps half an hour or more, and then there was a prolonged burst of gunfire that sounded deeper and heavier calibre than the rest, followed by a long silence.

Such incidents, especially in those waters, pose a dilemma. On the one hand there were likely to be injured and helpless people, a half-hour's steaming away or less, but on the other, we were not an armed vessel and, in any encounter with one carrying even light weapons, we would be pretty well helpless.

The blood-red twilight of the night-watch bridge was soon crowded with all manner of odd bodies, most of whom had no real reason to be there, aside from curiosity. In his bright little cupboard of a radio room, off the starboard side of the bridge proper, the radio operator was calling the mainland, reporting the incident to the authorities on the beach.

Piracy is a sensitive issue in the South China Sea. There was a short conference with the naval commander responsible for the area and then, as we half expected, we were 'requested' to give such aid as we could, prior to the arrival of a fast gunboat, or a vessel of the American Coastguard Service, to take over.

The captain was of course to have the final say and we were 'not to further endanger life', etc. But there was a clear tacit understanding that the national authorities expected the national oil company to perform, if, that is, it wanted to retain future contracts.

We took a great deal of interest in the radar picture. There were now three echoes, fairly well separated from each other, and two were receding fast towards the east. We pulled our divers off the job, recovered our reference weights, and began to move at slow ahead towards the nearest of the echoes.

It was already light when we made visual contact and of course we recognised the ship right away. How the junk had come so far to the west, far, far away from her intended course, we never learned, but the peeling blue-painted hull and the amazing, unseamanlike, houseboat style living quarters were unmistakable.

The derelict floated quietly in the water without wind or power to cause anything more than a slight rocking motion. The sun was showing the top quarter of its disc above the horizon, and the sea was mirror calm and pale gold. Of the other ships that the radar had picked up last night there was no sign.

We drifted closer under minimal power and ready to make a fast run for it, if this turned out to be a trap, but nothing stirred. After a few minutes of this cautious progress we cut power and drifted closer in near silence; the loudest sound was the slap of water and the soft rumble of our engines at dead slow.

Our deck was of course higher than the junk, so my first view was looking down at her from around six feet up. There was little sign of violence though, in a rough line across the sun-bleached deck planking, there was a stitched pattern of splintered tracks where the bullets had struck. Of the crew and the twenty or so refugees that she had carried there was no trace.

After a further wait to see if anyone might emerge from hiding we opened our service door, a steel watertight hatch around eight feet above the water line, and roughly in line with the junk's deck, and three men went aboard. We watched them poke gingerly about in the debris on the deck, turning up a pool of drying blood here and a few spent small arms cases there, and then, pushing aside the curtain that divided off the living area, they went inside.

Twenty seconds later they called for me on the radio. I had expected there to be injuries, but I was not prepared for the sight awaiting me inside that overheated little bamboo and reed shack.

Only the men were left, and I think that they had not expected what had happened to them, because, had they realised what was coming, they would surely have resisted, even if they knew that it was hopeless.

They sat, tied in a neat line against the rough walls of the cabin, naked for the most part. Each man had been killed with a single round to the head. Behind each one a splatter of blood on the reed wall showed that the bullet had been fired from close range and had exited through the back of the skull. On the wrist of one of the corpses was a recently applied plaster cast, my work of five days before.

In the far corner was the man who had introduced himself as the captain when we had last met. He alone had not been shot, instead someone had cut his throat for him. The smell of blood, hot and metallic, was in the air. I remember thinking that I should have felt nauseated but I was too angry for even that. These people had offered no harm to anyone, they had been killed for a few hundred in gold and their possessions because they had had the ill luck to run across men who were too stupid and too brutal to even understand the nature of the crimes that they had committed.

There had been some attempt to set the junk alight. A rough pile of cloth and paper in the middle of the floor was charred to ashes, but there had been too little that would burn, and the fire, instead of destroying the evidence, had simply gone out.

We searched below decks in the stinking waterlogged bilges where the old Leyland bus engine hulked in a pool of slimy water and leaked engine oil. There was nothing left alive, no man nor woman nor child, there was no trace of anyone left.

The facts of the situation were radioed in and we stood nervously by until an investigating officer could arrive. We were worried that the pirate vessel might return to complete the job of destruction. We had no doubt that they would monitor radio traffic and, with our help six hours' steaming away, would know that they had a margin of time in which to attack us.

The minutes dragged and every fish that splashed in the shade of the ship had men nervously checking the water. Almost alone among the crew old Billy remained unaffected. I tried to talk to him but his replies were monosyllabic, so I left him in the sun smoking and watching the fish jump under the canted bows of the junk.

The day wore on towards noon. The sun, always hot, gained strength and intensity. The camp boss prepared a massive Nassi Goreng for the midday meal, but I kept thinking about the bodies in that hot sweltering sun and I found I had lost most of my appetite.

At three in the afternoon help finally arrived, in the shape of a sleek fibreglass fast gunboat of the Malaysian Navy. A young officer, highly efficient in his knife-sharp creases, went aboard the wreck. To his credit he was still crisp when he came aboard to talk to us.

'There is really little to be done,' he said. 'They were refugees and so no one's responsibility. No one will admit that they were here and there are no survivors. We will sink the boat of course and bury the bodies here at sea. You are not diving on this site?'

'No,' said the skipper in a quiet voice. 'We're not diving on this site.'

'Good. Then I will arrange the formalities, Captain.'

'There is one thing,' I said as no one else seemed about to raise the point. 'There were women and children aboard when we encountered her last, what about them?'

'Alas, there is little I can do. We shall look of course and if we find evidence of piracy then we shall hang those responsible, but the people you mention will probably go to the slave markets in East Africa, or perhaps to brothels in India and the Gulf States.'

He paused and rubbed his immaculate manicured hand along his cheek, then he said, 'I understand that you would like to have helped, but, in all honesty, if you had been here last night there would have simply been more deaths.'

It was during the brief twilight when we buried them. The whole crew gathered to watch the wrapped and weighted bodies break the surface. When it was done we torched the wreck and left her to burn, settling slowly in the water like a funeral pyre for an old-time Viking warrior, before slowly flickering down to a few flaming timbers, and then, finally, there was nothing but the empty quiet sea.

Fred Jordan, the dive super, looked at it for a moment in silence and then, shaking himself as if awakening from a long reverie, he said, 'Right, you bastards have skived long enough. Back to work.'

12

The salvage job was finally proceeding to plan. The initial blowdown, the process that commits a saturation team of divers to four weeks enclosed under pressure in a set of large sealed steel chambers, had gone by the book. Of course it nearly always does, but I defy anyone to sit in front of the control panel and run in the high-pressure gases, without a slight butterfly stomach effect each time.

Salvage is quite a complex operation. It is not enough simply to plant explosives and spread the rig all over the ocean floor. There was a lot of good stuff to raise first. Moving loads around in a tangle of steel at the bottom of the sea is usually done by tuggers, air-driven winches that dangle lengths of steel cable down on to the work site below. The much heavier lift from the ship's crane is not often available under water. A crane wire, dipped in sea water, rusts and weakens, and with steel wires at several thousand pounds a time, no one chooses to destroy one on a simple lift.

Two days into the job, we were into the first major lift, the blow-out preventer, a complicated mechanism of valves and control gear worth a good deal of money, if we could raise it. The divers had rigged a spider's web of cables and strops, all leading to a single lifting wire that in turn was fed up to the tugger on deck. The idea was that a small explosive charge would break the blow-out preventer free of the rest of the wreck, while it swung from the tugger, and lifting bags would be attached to float it to the surface.

Explosives are always a disappointment to those whose expectations come from grainy, archive film of Second World War depth charges in action. A cutting charge hardly disturbs the surface and the only sound is a heavy clang as if some demon from the depths had hit the ship's underside with a heavy hammer.

It was when the divers returned to the site that we realised we still had a problem. As soon as we got a look at the TV pictures from below it was obvious that the charge had only partially done its job. There was still a great deal of steelwork holding the prize to the bottom. The right thing to do if that happens is to try the whole sequence again and to keep on trying until everything is fully free. But that does not allow for tight schedules, a fixed-price contract and the threat of an overrun to swallow all our profit.

Billy was running the dive and he decided on a short cut. The idea was that, if we pulled hard enough on the deck tugger, the remaining bits of steel that held the BOP down would break, and it would be free to move. A tug of war started between the winch driver and the wreck, but instead of six hefty blokes there were twenty tonnes of steel on one side and a thirty-five-tonne pull on the other. For two or three minutes nothing happened, by then the wire was pulled so tight that the oil squeezed out of the strands of cable and it made a high singing noise. The winch driver relaxed the tension a bit. But Billy seemed extraordinarily fixed on this idea.

'Try a quick jerk,' he said over the intercom.

Jerking a steel cable is maybe not one of the world's all-time great ideas. The tugger drum came to a grinding halt in a gasp of compressed air and the whole ship listed to port a little. The winch driver slacked off again. Billy, frustrated at the first attempt, ordered a diver back into the water to see what was holding the prize down. We waited for a time while the diver gradually worked around the body of the BOP trying to decide where it was trapped. Eventually suspicion centred on a chunk of steel I-beam lying on the control bundle that led away from the valves in a tangle of steel wires and torn hydraulic tubes. There was a hurried conference and it was decided to lower the load a tiny bit, taking the strain off the offending bundle so that it could be burned through with a cutting torch.

The winch driver relaxed and took himself off for a smoke while this went on, and, down below, the Broco torch ripped through the control bundle freeing the load. Then the diver, being the man on the spot, gave the order for the second attempt.

'Up a little on the tugger,' came the Tannoy voice from the bottom, distorted and high-pitched from the helium breathing mix.

'Roger. Coming up on the tugger.'

'All stop.'

'Stopped on the tugger.'

'Down on the tugger.'

'Coming down on the tugger.'

At that exact moment the welds that fixed the tugger to the deck, stressed way beyond the makers' intentions, gave out altogether. There was perhaps ten tonnes' pull on the wire at that point. The tugger unit, a boxy looking winch weighing all of a tonne, skated across the deck carrying with it the startled deck-hand who, against all regulations, had been sitting on the winch as he drove it. It slewed towards the gap in the rails where the wire passed overboard, screeching, tearing off paint, and trailing sparks as it went. The deck-hand, deciding that discretion was indeed the better part of valour, jumped off and ended up sitting on the deck watching it go.

Billy's language on the Tannoy was truly frightful as the tugger reached the rail, teetered for a long moment, and vanished over the side, landing with a mighty splash in the exact centre of the pool of bubbles that marked the position of our diver on the bottom.

There was a long expectant silence. All that we could hear was the bubble of gas through the regulator as the diver breathed in and out 300 feet below us. Then a voice cut in. Thin and distorted though it was, the irritation in the tone was unmistakable.

'Goddamnit, surface. I said "Down on the tugger", not "Send the bloody tugger down".'

* * *

On a dive ship there are very few places that a man can go to be alone during the working day. At night, though, the helideck is available. Its large flat open space is mostly unlit, clear of obstructions and deserted, so that, as long as one does not mind the ninety-foot drop over the unrailed sides, it makes a fine place to sit and watch the stars.

It was the time of the Pleiades meteorite storm that produces a brilliant display of pyrotechnics in the tropical skies every year. I am a poor astronomer but I find the night sky, with its endlessly turning wheel of stars, relaxing, and, in the Southern hemisphere, there is always the Southern Cross to marvel at.

Usually, no one else seems to share my enthusiasm for the tropical stars, and these trips up to the highest point of the ship, surrounded by twilight, high above a dark sea, are solitary pursuits. That night, there was someone else on the helideck by the time I got there. The meteor shower was at its height, and for a few minutes we watched the display in silence as green and red and golden sparks scratched their way across the dark velvet background of the night.

It was not until he lit a cigarette that I saw in the glow of the match that my late-night, star-watching companion was Billy Carson. It seems even now, long after the event, to be cowardly to admit that, of all the men on board, my best friend among them was the one I wanted to see least. But his illness had changed normal circumstances that trip.

'Pretty night,' he said.

'Beautiful. I've never seen a meteor shower so bright.'

'I never did thank you, mate.'

'Thank me. What for?'

'By rights, you should have told them, when you found out.'

'I don't think so.'

'No? Well, thanks anyway.'

He seemed a little drunk, but that was none of my affair either. I knew well enough that Billy was not above smuggling an illegal bottle aboard.

He said, 'How many have you seen die, Jon?'

'For Christ's sake . . .'

'No, really. You find it embarrassing to talk about, don't you?'

'Not embarrassing actually.'

''Course you do. Every bugger does. You know, that's the worst part. If I'd got the pox or something, I could shout it from the mess-room table, they wouldn't give a shit, but because I'm dying . . .'

'Billy. Leave it, mate, please. It's not that they don't care. If they knew they'd all . . .'

'All what, Jon? All pretend it wasn't happening? All talk about it in whispers. Even you can't admit it, can you?'

'All right. What do you want to talk about?'

'When they go. Are they afraid?'

'No, Billy, they aren't afraid, not when it comes to it. Mostly they just stop, as if someone had pulled a switch.'

'And after? Do you think there's something there?'

'Billy, that's not a fair question.'

He reached into his pocket and the starlight glinted on the bottle. He took a swallow and passed it across. I really didn't need it, but he needed me to take it, so I did. The stuff tasted like rocket fuel and burned right down to my stomach.

'Well,' he said, 'are you going to answer?'

'OK. I believe in something. Not the heavenly choirs and harps crap. But something. Yes, I believe that much.'

'Good. So do I.'

'Does it make it easier?' I asked.

'Not really. I have to leave behind all the things that I care about. I always thought that I might marry some day. I wanted to achieve something, anything I suppose.'

'But you have. You've lived more than twenty normal men. You've sailed the seas, you've visited most of the world, and you've learned so much, man.'

'Writing on water the Chinese call it. Soon there will be nothing left. If I'd had kids, kids who knew me, there would have been that at least. How old are yours now?'

'Eighteen and fourteen.'

'Grown up already. You know they say that a man who dies leaving sons only sleeps.'

'That sounds like a load of sexist crap to me, mate.'

'Still the reformer.'

'Sure. Why not?'

'Are you still trying to get a book published?'

'Yes.'

He looked up at the sky. The celestial display was fiercer than ever, so brilliant that occasionally a brighter than average flash would cast a shadow on the green-painted plating under our feet. He took another swig and passed the bottle over again. This time it went down more easily. Then he said, 'If you get published, will you put me in it?'

'If you like.'

'Tell a bit of it, mate. Tell the truth about how it was with us out here before they tidied it all up and made it a game safe for the children.'

'I'll tell it, Billy.'

He seemed to consider for a minute and then he started on another tack as if we had done with business for the night. He said, 'Do you remember in Bombay, when we raced those two taxis back from Leopold's and that Sikh taxi driver ran us all into a ditch?'

'And we had to bribe the police to let us go, in time to take the ship out next day.'

And we sat on, far into the night, swapping stories from the old times when he had first started and the divers were feeling their way, step by painful step, towards a safe way of doing the most dangerous job on earth. And, to my shame and bitter regret, I fell asleep there on the warm metal of the helideck, with the tropical stars burning holes in the night over my head, and when I woke with the sour taste of bad booze in my mouth, and a slight throbbing ache behind my eyes, he was gone and I never saw him again.

We searched of course. The ship steamed the square pattern that covers the open ocean to the best advantage, but, although we scanned the gentle sea with professional zeal, and although we did everything that the rules said that we should, we found nothing.

Officially it was accidental. After a brief simple quasi-legal inquiry, he was marked on the muster as 'Discharged Dead'. His own doctor knew well enough that he was on borrowed time, but I was able to confirm that he had been drinking that night, and there are no rails on the helideck, and the sea is ninety feet below. In the end, I suppose that it was the way he would have wanted it. Through accident or design the sea had the final say, and there was nothing left except maybe a few new stories that are a part of the legend, and, when all is said and done, few enough of us achieve even that suspect immortality.

13

We were behind our schedule by three weeks now, and in the end we decided to blow up the rest of the wreck in situ and forgo any other salvage that might have been raised. The contract stated that no debris could protrude from the seabed by more than twelve feet, and flattening the 15,000-tonne structure was not going to be easy. It is very rarely possible simply to put a huge charge of explosives against a steel structure and hope to flatten it. In reality the charges need to break particular welds so that the whole thing falls under its own weight. There were thirty of these to blow, all but one accessible to divers without any real difficulty. The thirtieth weld, number thirteen on the builder's drawings, was buried under fifteen feet of mud.

So we had to build ourselves an air lift, which is, in effect, a hollow tube about a foot across at the open end with a smaller pipe running down the side of it. We pump high-pressure air down the smaller pipe, and the rush of bubbles up the wider tube creates a current that sucks water, mud, stones and light debris up from the bottom and spews them out in a plume at the top of the lift for the water to take away. We soon had a rough working system rigged from a piece of twenty-inch hose and a long section of high-pressure air line. It looked like a bad dream of Heath Robinson's, but, when the air compressor was started, with the open end submerged in the sea, a very satisfying rush of water and foam spewed into the air from the free end.

Properly managed a lift can dig a sizeable hole in the seabed in a few hours, but there is a down side. The hole that the lift creates is saucer shaped, and as it gets deeper it tends to fall in on itself. It's possible to reduce this effect by widening the hole but that slows things down and it becomes a fine judgement call as to how large the hole must be. Too large and time mounts up against you, too small and the shaft that develops in the ocean floor can collapse in on itself and ruin a day's work in seconds.

It looked as if the air lift was about to be the answer to our problems. With its open end close to the surface of the ooze the mud rushed into the airstream at a satisfying rate and soon a discoloured plume of water stretched a good half-mile from our work site as the disturbed mud drifted in the current before settling back to the bottom.

It was this apparent smile on the face of whatever gods oversee diving vessels that made everyone involved just a little careless. The mud was just too good to be true, it was soft enough for the lift to shift it easily but still firm enough to hold its structure as the shaft into the seabed grew gradually deeper and we exposed more and more steelwork in the area of weld thirteen.

On the second day the shaft was around twelve feet deep and rather than the normal saucer shape it was about eight feet across, and very near vertical sided. We took to positioning the open bottom door of the diving bell above the hole so that it was very simple for the bell man to watch progress and monitor the diver's activities. The ROV was close into the work site, providing a little extra light and nosing around the steelwork in a fussy kind of robotic ballet.

At about four in the morning the air lift hit a cavity in the mud. The softer fill within the cavity was whisked out in an instant by the rush of air, and the shaft wall, deprived of its support, began to collapse in slow motion.

The diver, twelve feet below the seabed and concentrating on the action of the air lift, had no time to do more than open the diverter valve of his helmet. This at least meant that as long as we could pump fresh breathing gas to him he would not drown.

There was a great dark coloured plume of mud in the water above the shaft. The air lift belched and screamed, loaded far beyond its capacity to shift mud, and the compressors, protected by their electronic overload cut-outs, stopped with a great hiss of offloaded compressed air.

The sudden silence was as loud as a thunderclap out of a blue sky. On the bottom the ROV nosed closer to inspect the damage. The displaced mud was clearing rapidly now in the five-knot current that washed over the work site. The steelwork was there just the same and there sticking out of the mud among the debris was the tube of the air lift. But of the diver and the shaft where he had been working there was no sign, apart from a depression in the seabed where the shaft had been, and his umbilical lines sticking up out of the mud.

On that particular ship the dive control room is shared with saturation control and because of that I could hear and see everything that took place in those first few minutes.

George, the Aussie who was supervising the dive, was cool and sensible. No hint of panic in that flat, friendly voice.

'Right, diver two. Time to earn your bonus. Your mate has got himself buried in the mud. Get out and dig.'

'On my way, surface. Do you have communications with diver one?'

George flipped the switches that would connect him to the buried man.

'Diver one, do you copy?'

No response, just the empty idiot hiss of random static.

'Diver one. Do you copy?'

Still nothing. He played delicately with the controls of the communications set as if he might coax a response.

'Diver one, surface. Come back.'

There was a rattle of static and under it the suggestion of cadenced speech. He turned to me, 'Do you think that he responded then?'

'Could be,' I said. 'The fall might have dislodged his plug and knocked out his output.'

He turned back to the set.

'Diver one. We are unable to make anything of your comms. Diver two is at the moment working to free you and we will feed gas until he does. If you can relax and wait for help, we will reach you as soon as we can.'

He flipped the switch.

'Diver two, how are you doing?'

The voice was tinny and squawky with helium but quite clear.

'The mud is softer than it was to start with and I've got his umbilical to guide me in. I guess I should reach him in about three or four hours.'

'OK, diver two. As fast as you can, mate.'

The trapped man was probably still alive, being gently crushed by the weight of the suffocating mud. If his partner could not reach him in time that mud would eventually fill his regulator exhaust and he would be unable to exhale. There was nothing we could do to help the diver on the bottom reach his mate before the time ran out. But there were preparations to make on the surface.

We always keep one chamber of the main pressure complex empty and unpressurised so that if the worst happens the duty medic can be sent down to the divers' living depth so that there is no delay in treatment.

I spent the last few minutes before the start of pressurisation checking that I had all the gear that I was likely to need and that it was not sealed in any way at all. It is vital that gas can enter all containers as the pressure increases. Otherwise it will simply crush anything hollow within the system. The instruments lay on the steel table, arranged in kits. The outer door closed with a thud and the voice of my opposite number came over the speaker above my head.

'Ready for blowdown, inside?'

'As ready as I'll ever be.'

'Roger that. Good luck, mate. Going for a seal.'

The gas came in with a roar and the door that had swung free a few seconds before was suddenly sealed tight. The gas pressure built quickly and I held my nose and blew hard against the obstruction to equalise the differential in my ears, there was a squeak that was felt rather than heard and the discomfort vanished. At the depth I was going to, it would be three days, eleven hours and twenty-five minutes before the door could be opened again. I sat down to wait.

Although the chamber complex was spotlessly clean inside, it smelled of the sea and of recirculated air. The incoming gas raised the temperature as the pressure grew higher and by the time I reached bottom depth it was as hot and clammy as a rain forest before a storm breaks, which are the conditions that divers accept as part of their normal working day, but for the practice of emergency medicine they are not ideal.

Leading off the chamber, through the steel hatchway that was now held only by the safety clips designed to stop the hundred-kilo doors moving in high seas, was a smaller rounded pressure chamber perhaps eight feet across and ten high. In the roof of this chamber was a further pressure door, operated by a hydraulic ram. It was to the collar on the other side of the door that the bell would mate when the time came.

Reports of progress on the bottom came over the intercom loud and clear, now unaffected by helium distortion.

'Diver two has uncovered him. Apparently he's still breathing but there isn't any sign that he's conscious. Wait, one chamber' – a period of crackling static with the ghosts of voices hidden in it – 'OK. He's got him freed and is using the man lift to get him back into the bell. There were bubbles from his exhaust up till a couple of minutes ago but now there's nothing. As far as he can tell, the casualty is out cold.'

'OK,' I said to the overheard pick-up, 'I copy all of that, surface. How long before I can get at him?'

'Bell is leaving bottom depth now. Say three minutes hauling time at emergency speed. Two minutes to lock on. He should be with you in ten minutes at the outside.'

'OK, look that's too long if he isn't breathing. Has diver two taken off his helmet?'

'Affirmative.'

'Right, get diver two to use the emergency oxygen to force some gas into him.'

'Wait, one chamber . . . OK. He's breathing without oxygen, but his colour is poor and he's not responsive to pain.'

This report showed that the second diver was medically trained. Soon that might really matter, but lack of response to pain is not a good sign. It suggests profound unconsciousness. One step from brain injury.

Overhead there were clanking and rumbling sounds and then a heavy solid clang as the bell engaged on to its mating collar. For a few seconds there was silence, as they tested the mating collar and its interlocks to make sure that the seal was good. If the bell were to blow off, and it has happened on occasions, there would be more than one casualty to worry about, not that I would be around to help. After what seemed a long wait, but was really only three minutes or so, there was the familiar sound of gas rushing into the collar so that the door to the bell could be opened. From the steel hatch directly above there was a brief shower of icy sea water as the seal went, an almost insignificant puff of incoming gas that registered as a barely felt pressure change in my ears, and then the hydraulics were hissing and chuffing to themselves and the door swung open.

The lights inside the steel chamber of the bell were dim yellow in comparison to the hard bright white of the transfer lock. The injured man was hanging by his harness from the recovery winch, looking for all the world like a gibbeted corpse. The winch rattled and squealed as the body slowly ratcheted down through the collar into the system proper.

Diver two was Andy, another Australian, and he was already giving me a report on action taken so far.

'He was out cold when I found him and buried rolled in a ball in the mud. As far as I could see his gas feed was OK, but there wasn't much from the exhaust so I don't know how much flow he was getting. When I first took his hat off I thought that he was awake but it was maybe just reflexes. Since then nothing. His pulse is steady but it's one ten and I couldn't do a BP reading.'

'Mate, that's bloody marvellous, you did a great job. Now we need to get him stripped and on to a bunk where we can get a good look at him.'

The dressing shears that normally slice denim jeans like tissue paper were no match for the combination of tough rubber hot-water suit and a neoprene undersuit inside that. So there was no help for it but to manoeuvre him out of the diving gear as best we could, risking unknown fractures and internal injuries to do it, but finally we had him naked on the bunk.

There were few external signs of injury, a little bruising from the pressure of the metal collar on the side of his neck and a reddish livid-looking mark over the right side but nothing spectacular. No bleeding, no fluid loss, even his pulse was slowing a little, yet he was still profoundly unconscious.

It was no good yearning for the equipment of a hospital Intensive Care Unit. In offshore medicine God helps only those who help themselves, so we set to.

We washed him and ran our hands over his body, paying attention to the joints and bones to feel for any abnormalities. There was only one finding that mattered, and Andy found it first. There was a small area of skin just above the left collar bone that felt odd.

He touched my hand and gestured. 'Feel him here, mate,' he said. 'What do you think?'

The skin was clear, no bruising marred the light tan but there was an odd squashy feel to the underlying flesh and a few small pockets that felt as if someone had scattered puffed rice grains under the skin.

'Oh shit. Crepitus.'
'That's what I thought myself.'
'OK. Well, we have to drain it.'

There was gas under his skin, and gas in that position could only have come from a lung, tracking its way up through the loose flesh of the mediastinum where the lungs and heart join and are cushioned in a pocket of membrane behind the breastbone.

On the surface, where such gas indicates a punctured lung, it might just be permissible to leave the situation to stabilise, but at sea, and under pressure, things are more complex. If we left him untreated, and reduced the pressure on his body in order to quit the system, that small pocket of gas would obey Boyle's law and get bigger. As it did, it would force itself a larger and larger space inside the man's chest until, in the end, the affected lung would collapse. Left unchecked the gas pocket would then track across his chest and repeat the lethal effect on the other side.

Traumatic bilateral tension pneumothorax is the technical name for it but the bottom line is that, unchecked, it's a killer.

The trick is to release the gas, allowing it to escape from the man's chest as he is decompressed and vent harmlessly away, but to do that one needs to make a hole in the chest wall.

We do carry the necessary equipment of course, and, in theory, every diving medic can perform a thoracentesis to allow the escape of trapped gas, but very few of us ever do one in practice. We swabbed over the chest wall on the left side with iodine solution. This is both a good antiseptic and stains the skin yellow, so that it is obvious which bits are sterile.

It was not possible to set up an operating theatre type sterile field, so we used an alternative method, antiseptic surgery, the forerunner of modern methods that relies on the destruction of micro-organisms rather than their exclusion, to protect against infection.

I made the first cut, rather tentatively, and, although it drew a fine line of blood from the skin, it did not expose the intercostal muscle between the ribs as it should have done. There is no doubt that if you are not a trained surgeon, it is difficult to cut into the flesh of another human being. The second try was better. The skin divided to disclose a thin layer of yellowish fat and, underlying that, the deep red of muscle. In days past I would have had to go further, cutting through the muscle itself to produce a small hole through the chest wall to allow the passage of a length of clear plastic tubing into the chest cavity itself.

The tube is then led into a water trap to allow air out but not in. Instead of this rather cumbersome piece of equipment we were able to use a small and simple one way valve with a razor sharp point to penetrate the chest wall.

The needle on the business end of the valve sank quickly and easily into the chest. There was a small rush of air and a little blood. I closed the cut with a couple of stitches and left the valve in place. So far so good, chest drain in place, gas flowing out, patient still comatose.

We went over the surface of his skull time and again, looking for the tell-tale soft spots that might mean fractures. Time and again we raised flaccid eyelids and flashed lights on to perfectly reactive pupils to check for a one-sided response to light. His chest rose and fell in a steady rhythm, his heartbeat a regular slow tattoo, there was no sign of complication from the lung injury, and the antibiotics that we pumped into him as a precaution seemed to have staved off infection, and still he remained maddeningly unresponsive.

In the end, after a full day of tests, and consultation with the beach, we decided to decompress. There really was no reason not to. Everything that could be done under pressure was done and in any case the consensus, carefully not articulated but only hinted at, was that the loss of oxygen during those last few minutes before rescue had destroyed a vital area of brain function – the ultimate nightmare in trauma work. As the decompression progressed Andy grew withdrawn, and took to reading endless paperback books on a curtained bunk, trying to ignore the situation altogether.

We were twenty hours or so from the surface when he finally talked about it.

'I should have bloody left him, mate,' he said.

'No. No, you did right.'

'Balls I did. Bloody look at him. He won't come out of it, will he?'

We looked across at our patient. He seemed so normal. If it had not been for the yellow urinary drain tube snaking out from under the sheet, and the IV line, he might have been merely asleep.

'You couldn't know it would happen this way,' I said. 'A few minutes either way is all it takes.'

It was maybe three or four hours later when we heard the sounds. We were trying to sleep when they started. Patients in coma do make noises. They belch and rumble and fart and cough, all of them automatic functions, but this was a groan and a broken mumble, that sounded like a man talking in his sleep.

I was by his side in a moment. His lips were smacking and he
pawed at the air as if the light hurt his eyes. After a few moments
his eyelids flickered and opened.

He said, 'Jon. What the hell are you doing in here?' And then as
reality hit, and with it memory, 'Oh Jesus, the mud. Can I have a
drink?'

'Sure.'

As I held the water for him I caught sight of Andy. There was
an expression of wonder on his face and two shiny tracks down his
cheeks.

'Are you really OK, mate?' he finally asked.

'Damn right, you Aussie bastard. What took you so long to get
me out?'

*   *   *

We steamed back around the sand bar into Miri on a day so full of
soft grey mist that it seemed that the whole world was water, and the
song of the frogs beside the river was loud, and raucous. Out in the
South China Sea, a barge, loaded with the salvaged remains of the
platform, was sailing back towards Taiwan. The dive ship nudged
into the wharf among the godowns along the waterfront. Nothing
was changed, the loafers and the marijuana sellers were still there,
but Billy was gone, and his absence clouded our homecoming.

There is a tradition in the industry that if a man dies on the job,
his friends gather in one of the divers' bars, to hold a wake to mark
his passing. These are not affairs known for their good order, in fact
some bars, establishments whose terrible reputations are known to
seafarers the world over, have blanched at the idea of hosting such
an event.

The Cosy Inn, warned in advance, had closed its bar 'for essential
repairs' that night, and, in the end, the event was held in the 'Rancho
Grande' room.

For three hours it was relatively peaceful. A few of the party
were maudlin drunk, a few were stoned on the local hash, and a
few called for food (the food it must be said was excellent), and
then the fireworks made an appearance.

It is something that divers share with the Orientals, this love of
loud explosions in small spaces. In the East fireworks are religious.
Loosing off strings of firecrackers is a way of destroying and scaring
away the demons that lurk unseen in the very air that surrounds us.
An Eastern funeral is often hidden in clouds of pungent blue powder

smoke, and the wails of the professional mourners are drowned by the rattling and banging.

Eastern firecrackers are not like Western bangers. In the UK generations of control and legislation have reduced the risk of handling fireworks to a minimum for those with a grain of common sense. In the East firecrackers come in long tangled strings with bright red fuses that burn in a totally unpredictable fashion, slowly one second, and racing along the next, leaping from tube to tube of powder, each bang louder than the last, until, finally, at the very end of the string, it reaches the thumb-thick, six-inch long monster of a cracker that ends the show with a massive detonation. Not the sort of thing to let off in a bar, unless you're a diver. After all, it was Billy's funeral.

At first it was harmless enough, it just sounded like a cross between World War Three and a bad day in Vietnam. The bar filled with choking fumes, but everyone, even the bar owner, who had sold his entire stock, and had to send out for more, thought it funny. But they never know when to stop.

In the corner, Jimmy, a skinny young Glaswegian, who loved explosives the way a man might love women, began to hatch a truly spectacular end to the evening. I only found out exactly what he had done later, but, in essence, he simply emptied the powder from a half-dozen of the biggest tubes and, with the help of an old cigar case and salvaged bits of fuse, constructed a mother of all firecrackers. I imagine that he intended to light the thing and throw it into the air, so that it exploded near the ceiling, giving maximum bang with minimum damage, but in a room twelve feet high or less, that calls for a very short fuse.

The explosion was devastating. It blew men flat, blackened the floor, scorched the ceiling, smashed all the lights and filled the air full of unbreathable sulphur fumes.

I found myself outside in the rain. I still don't remember getting there. Jimmy was holding his right hand in his left and there was blood on his fingers.

'Away and shite,' he said in a disgusted voice, 'I blew ma bloody fingers off.'

It wasn't quite that bad. The amputation of the top joint of his first finger was clean and the second was simply bruised, as if someone had thumped it with a hammer. It was clearly not a good time to hang about. There were police sirens in the distance.

We scattered. The ship was near enough to be a safe haven, and it was there that we gathered over the next hour, creeping in out of the dark and the wet to dress the injuries and assess the damage.

Fred was livid, not just angry but close to homicidal. At one stage I was more in danger of losing my patient to murder by his superior than from shock.

Repairing finger ends is relatively easy, even if carrying out the operation after a five-hour party does not improve the performance, but by the time the sun was burning the morning mists off the river, the finger looked OK. Not a great job to be sure, but not a bad one. Outside, it sounded as if the local police were holding a riot drill. We went below to a cold, deserted galley to raid the stores for breakfast.

We were still sitting there when a member of the Filipino crew came in.

'Ah, you are all safe then,' he said by way of greeting.

'Yes,' I replied. Pretended innocence seemed the best way.

'You hear what happen in town last night?'

'No.'

'Terrorists attacked a bar or they say maybe it was drug barons.'

'Really. Anybody hurt?'

'No one. Lucky, yes?'

'Very,' I agreed, trying not to meet Fred's eyes.

On the plane home, safely out of Malay jurisdiction, we held a collection for a cheque to pay for the repairs to the bar; but all the way, even through the ever-friendly British Customs at Heathrow – 'Morning, lads. Good trip?' – Jimmy kept my perfect bandaging job carefully under wraps in his jacket pocket.

14

It is a mistake to return to a place that once held magic. Bombay, with its endless spirituality and insane, laid-back, working practices, had been, for me, such a place. I would never have returned if anyone but Gerry Mason had asked me.

After the team dispersed at the end of the Miri job there was a period of deathly quiet. These seem to affect the diving industry from time to time, leaving crews stranded on the beach and waiting for months while skills and dive systems rust with disuse. Because we live far away from each other, at these times teams are reduced to distant voices on the phone. Inevitably, as time passes, the tight-knit structure that holds groups together gradually disintegrates.

Gerry had kept a low profile since the breakdown of his marriage. So low a profile in fact that while I was peripherally aware of his doings from the gossip of mutual friends, our paths never seemed to cross. However, Gerry was still a working dive boss and, fortunately for me, still regarded me as to some extent his protégé.

'Bombay High,' he said, over a phone line that sounded as if little green men had hijacked the satellite. 'As soon as you can, mate. I've booked you on two flights so if you don't make tonight, the overnight tomorrow will do.'

Gerry's first booking was just three hours UK time after the phone call and it was a non-starter. The following night, at midnight, the big 747 lumbered into the night sky over London and I was on my way.

It was in some ways like revisiting an old lover, only to find that time and divergent life experiences have destroyed whatever of the old affection might have survived the years. Bombay was different. Leopold's was full of tourists, served burgers and had waiters in American-style paper hats. The street people were fewer. The corruption, always a feature in Bombay, had lost its innocence.

The papers shrieked thick black headlines about gangsters, about murder, about the twentieth century. Bombay was a frontier that had closed its doors on its raw past and embraced a newer, more sophisticated notion of civilisation.

But Gerry was the same. Still easy-going, still drinking, still one of the best in the world in his own chosen area of expertise. We sailed out into the welcoming waters of Bombay High, and there at least, out at sea, India was unchanged.

Towards the end of a job that, by Indian standards, was a model of smooth efficiency, with the spectre of renewed unemployment a clear possibility, Gerry had a proposition for me.

'You'll like this job,' he said. 'Just up your street. It's in the back of beyond, but then you and civilisation never did really mix, did you?'

'Sounds good,' I said, determined not to let Gerry's lunatic sense of humour get a rise out of me.

'Where is this job?'

'Vietnam,' he said and grinned.

'Vietnam?'

'I thought I just said that.' He was enjoying himself.

'What is it?' I asked. 'Salvage?'

'No. Oil.'

'Oil? Off Vietnam?'

'Yep. And you'll love the company. It's a real star this one.'

'Go on,' I said.

'Well,' said Gerry, 'it's called the South China Sea Oceanic Salvage and Towing Company.'

'Good God,' I said.

'I do hope so,' said Gerry, 'I really do.'

                              *   *   *

Waking in the company's rest-house at Coa Long, eighty miles from the coast, it was difficult to realise it used to be bandit country in earnest, during the long cruel years of the American War. It is always the 'American War' because, to the Vietnamese, it was merely the latest in a long line of wars of independence. And Ho Chi Minh, who rose from being an obscure pastry cook in London's China Town to be the father of a finally united nation, was just one more war leader, in a long line of war leaders, whose only distinction was that he finally united a country divided by foreign intervention.

Vietnam is a peaceful, gentle country whose fate has been bloody, endless wars. They have always been at war, these people, against the warlords from the north, against the hill tribes from Laos and finally against the massive power of the Americans.

The route into the country is difficult because none of the airlines with US connections fly to Ho Chi Minh City, and in the end, our circuitous route took us via Singapore to Malaysia, and thence to Cambodia, where a charter pilot who seemed anxious to pretend that his destination was elsewhere than Vietnam, flew us in.

There are a great many charter pilots in that part of the world and many of them use small planes, with small radar shadows to make a good, if dangerous, living out of flying opium and its products out of the Golden Triangle.

Our pilot was American or, at least, I think he was. He spoke with a down home accent so thick it was hard to tell just what he was talking about. He wore aviator sunglasses, even at night, faded bush camouflage, and army fatigue boots with a great many shiny buckles that tinkled as he walked. Also he had the disconcerting habit of smoking the local hashish while he was flying. It might have calmed his nerves but it did nothing for those of his passengers.

From the airport where, thirty years ago, the Americans made their last stand, they drove us, cross country, through a darkness that smelled of the jungle and the wet, to the old French colonial house that was to act as the shore rest base while we were in Vietnam. At one point it must have been magnificent, now, with its creaking mosquito shutters, and cranky generator that always cut at the most inopportune moment, it looked like a set from a Tarzan film.

The jungle had not so much taken over as crept up on Coa Long. The place was not overwhelmed, merely absorbed into the surrounding vegetation. But it was big and there were enough rooms for one each, and there was also a diminutive Vietnamese and his wife to look after us, or the house.

Morning in a new country is always a time of discovery. One of the great joys of the diving industry is that we are often far from the tourist track. This morning was no exception. I woke a good while before the others. Jet-lag doesn't bother me, maybe because I always sleep on planes. It was quiet, with the peacefulness you only get at that time of day. On the raised veranda outside the door there were rough benches where you could sit and look out across the countryside. The air was full of a very light mist, so gauzy it was barely evident. The jungle was green, so incredibly lush, the leaves had almost a blue cast to them, as if they were charged with the rich juices of manic growth, almost to bursting. Perhaps a half-mile off, the paddies stretched endlessly, in a neat mosaic of water and dams all softened by that gauzy mist.

Away behind us animals called in the jungle; later I found that they were monkeys greeting the new day by staking their claim to a food tree in their area. The rising sun gilded the low lying mists red and gold. It was a picture from a willow-pattern world, so fragile, so delicate that it looked as if a heavy-footed Westerner might destroy it, simply by walking across the tracks.

It was hard to imagine such a place torn by war, inciner- ated by Napalm, raped by the rolling thunder that fell from the B52s which flew too high even to see. Yet this had been a killing field. A hundred kilometres from here was a sleepy insignificant hamlet called My Lai where an obscure field com- mander called William Caley had let his panic rule his trigger finger.

Mr Nugyen, the man who looked after the place, materialised behind me.

'You rise early,' he said.

'Yes. I wanted to see the sun come up.'

'You are a poet or a painter perhaps?'

'No, sadly not.'

'It is not sad surely to look on beauty while it is before us? You will take tea?'

'Please.'

Green tea came in a bowl of pure white porcelain, its aromatic steam perfuming the morning. It was a week before we joined the ship, a week in the country, and each morning I took my chance to watch the sun come up and drank my bowl of green tea in the soft blue light of another day.

It was a mistake to get friendly with the old man and his wife. Vietnam is not a country for Westerners to have friends, but from that first morning, when he philosophised about the nature of ephemeral beauty in his oddly accented English, we were friends whether we liked it or not.

Over a few days I found out a little about him and how he had come to be liaison and housekeeper for a diving company based across the waters in Singapore, as we talked in the bright sunlight of the old French graveyard, behind the house, where eight long-dead expatriates fertilised the soil of the land that they had sought to exploit.

He had, it seems, once worked for the Vietnamese police American liaison section which explained his knowledge of English. These same police, who were known to the troops and the Vietnamese themselves as 'White Mice' from the white uniforms they wore, were a byword for high-level corruption and casual brutality. With the fall of Saigon in the last days of the war he had been captured and 're-educated' in an up-country camp where the daily lessons consisted pretty well entirely of readings from Chairman Mao's tedious Little Red Book. Finally they had released him, and more or less forgotten his existence. His first wife had disowned him in the early days of the new regime, and so he had begun again. A small-time administrator in a country that had no further interest in his skills, a small-time businessman in a country where entrepreneurs were social criminals.

Somehow he had survived, a few days' work here and a few there kept him alive. Twice he had attempted the dangerous crossing to Hong Kong and failed in both attempts. One day at a government office where he worked as a cleaner he learned there was a need for a Vietnamese who could be trusted and could speak English well. His political loyalty was of course suspect, but in the end his knowledge of the language had been enough, and so here he was, at the rest-house.

In return for this flood of detail I told him very little. Talking too openly in places with oppressive regimes has cost many a man his work permit and his job. I did however let slip that I was the team medic. Two days afterwards Gerry sought me out.

'There's a job for you out front, mate,' he said.

'A job? Here?'

'Sure. You did tell the old man you were a medic.'

'Oh no.'

It was a woman of indeterminate age, wearing the black pyjamas of the peasant labourers, and she was leading a young girl of perhaps eight or nine years old. Of course neither spoke a word of English but the trouble was clear enough. The woman folded back the cuff of the girl's trouser leg to expose the right calf and an ugly tropical ulcer perhaps a half-inch across. I have seen these often enough in India where they are called 'rupara' because they take on the shape and size of a rupee coin. They are painful, ugly, intractable lesions that often require repeated courses of antibiotics to clear them up, as they are frequently invaded by opportunistic organisms that attack the raw wound site and set up a complex of infections.

There was a brief interchange of singsong speech and the old man translated for me. The girl had been bitten by a leech in the fields, the wound had infected, and this was the result. They had already treated it with clean dressings and plant-based remedies, but now the girl was sick.

I opened my bag to reveal the usual display of bright stainless steel and packaged drugs. Her temperature was first on the list. Thirty eight point two. Not terrible, but high. The glands under her chin and in her armpits were already up; I didn't risk offence by checking, but I was sure that the big lymph glands in her groin would be up too.

'She has a generalised infection,' I said to the old man, and he translated the sense of that to the woman.

'She must take these tablets, three, three times each day.' I sorted out a five-day course of Ampicillin and handed them over.

They walked away towards the village and Gerry came over to talk to me.

'Is she OK?' he asked.

'Yes. It's a nasty infection, but we caught it early. She'll be better in a day or two.'

'Don't make a habit of it, will you, mate?'

'Of course not, but the kid did need help.'

'Did you hear what happened to Glen off the *Samphire*?'

'No, I've not seen him for months.'

'Well, he treated a kid, just like you did, but the kid died, and Glen ended up jail for six weeks while it got sorted out.'

'You could have told me before I did the job on her.'

'You'd have treated her in any case.'

Of course it was all right. The mother brought her back a few days after to show me a neat crusted scab where the ulcer had fulminated on her leg, and by then the kid was walking well and the temperature was gone, but even so I took good care about treating Vietnamese locals after that.

On the Saturday the village headman invited us to his house for a meal in appreciation of our efforts, and that was how I came across the most troubling case of all.

The meal was odd in itself. We were all dressed in our cleanest clothes and we sat on the floor around a matting cloth loaded with dishes of all kinds of unfamiliar foodstuffs. We had taken the old man along to translate. Of course most of what was said was pleasantries on both sides that meant very nearly nothing, until there was an interruption. A young woman had been hanging around outside the doorway and from time to time she gestured to the women who were serving the meal. The headman waved her away once or twice and shouted a few words in Vietnamese but she stayed despite what was clearly a rebuke. In the end I asked our translator what was going on.

'She wants the Westerners to look at her baby,' he said. 'But there is no point. It would be useless to you and not helpful to her.'

'What is wrong with the kid?'

'It has the American sickness, from after the planes years ago.'

'But I thought that you said it was a baby. The raids were twenty years and more ago.'

'Yes, I did.'

At that point the headman, who had evidently followed some of this exchange, cut in in rapid dialect. The old man listened for a few moments and then he said, 'He says that you may see the child if you wish. Perhaps you have never seen this sickness before.'

The headman led the way across an open space where half the village seemed to be gathered to watch. He passed through the small crowd of giggling women and impassive children holding an oil lamp high in his hand, and he seemed pleased, almost proud, to be able to display a sight that the Westerners might find new and diverting.

The hut was dim and there were deep shadows in the corners and a smell of warm humanity. There was a single oil lamp for lighting and, beside the sleeping area, a small crib with a child in it.

The headman, who had accompanied us in, took the lamp and held it close to the baby. Right away I could see that the head was all wrong. Occasionally, in the development of a human foetus, a group of defects arise in the tubular structure that becomes the spinal cord and the brain. In many cases these neural tube defects lead to spontaneous abortion very early in pregnancy, and in those that do not the most common effect is spina bifida and hydrocephalus, where fluid circulation in the brain's ventricles fails and causes a build-up of pressure within the skull. But this was something else. The infant was clearly very young indeed, a few days at most, and the reddish scar of the umbilical cord was still unhealed. To the level of the eyebrows the body was quite normal, though there was not a lot in the way of muscle tone, but above that level there was only ruin.

Where the vault of the skull should have been domed, and marked only by the soft central area of the fontanelle, this skull was misshapen, collapsed, as if above eye level there was nothing within the braincase. I took a look into the eyes with the ophthalmoscope from the kit. There were reflexes but they were sluggish at best. Then I looked into the left ear, and there was nothing to see, only disorganised tissue.

'Oh, God. Anencephaly,' I said.

'You have seen this before?' Gerry asked from well back in the shadows.

'Never seen it. I've read about it once or twice.'

'So what is it?'

'No brain tissue. The kid has an empty skull.'

'And he's alive?'

'No. Not really. The spinal cord reflexes are there so he can breathe and his blood circulates but in a few days he'll die, or at least his body will. This one was never really alive at all.'

Back at the rest-house it was a subdued little gathering around the table in the bright yellow light of the electric bulb. They were all tough men but everyone, myself included, had found the sight of that profoundly damaged kid disturbing.

So this was the result of Agent Orange, the defoliation programme that was contaminated with dioxins because they needed a lot more than the domestic industry could make and brought the stuff in from all over, some of it none too pure.

'But it did that to that kid? Twenty years after? How long will it last?' asked Garry, our single American.

'Dioxin? Maybe thirty years, maybe a hundred, no one really knows, but it's stable and hard to decontaminate, even if they could afford to try, so I suppose the problem will last a while yet.'

Garry took a pull at his beer.

'Thirty goddamn years?' he said.

He was still sitting there after we all gave up on the night and went to bed.

*   *   *

The night before we were due to join the ship everyone took the chance of a last uninterrupted bull session around a table full of beers, one of those occasions where old stories, or new versions of them, get passed around from man to man.

Gerry was well into a cautionary tale about a man whose depression on a long trip had led him eventually to suicide, when I noticed a small movement in the shadows behind his chair. The rest-house décor was heavily into tropical hardwoods with rich red-brown beams and floors that shone like clear honey. At one time it might have been the library of a French colonial planter and the whole wall was lined with a complex mass of joinery supporting shelves, small cupboards and niches.

It was in the shadows of that structure that something had moved. It was a fairly small something – 'perhaps a mouse,' I thought at first – and I watched it as Gerry went on with his story.

'We were worried by then, mind,' he said, ''cause after the way he'd behaved the night before, we reckoned that anything might happen, so we had decided that when he came off shift we'd get a few drinks down him and see if we could cheer him up a bit.'

In the shadows the thing became more definite. It was perhaps eight inches or so long and from the scintilla of reflections in the lamplight it possessed tiny ruby red eyes with which to observe the gathering beneath it and maybe savour the quality of the storytelling.

'. . . We were all sat there,' Gerry was saying, 'and a right bloody miserable occasion it was too. Him as pissed off as a pork butcher at a bar mitzvah, and the rest of us trying not to say anything that might make it worse . . .'

Behind Gerry's head the creature came out into the light for the first time. It was a spider, and by the way its bristles shone in the light and its eyes glowed with health it was a spider in the full prime of life.

'. . . Anyhow, the night dragged on, and by three in the morning we was reckoning that he'd had so much to drink that he wasn't going anywhere, even if he felt like it, so we wedged him in his bunk, with his head over the edge a bit in case he should throw up, and . . .'

The spider gave the impression that it was sitting up and cleaning its whiskers, like a rabbit in an English clover patch. Then it began a complex set of ballet movements with its front pair of legs, raising first one, then the other, then both together and waving them energetically from side to side as if signalling to an unseen audience.

Gerry was unaware that he was losing his audience, for Keith sitting beside me was also mesmerised by the performing spider, which was now executing a move like a man winding up to throw a hammer. Quite oblivious to the rival attraction, Gerry was building up to his punch line.

'We searched all over the bloody ship but in the end it was obvious he had topped himself and there was a fifty-tonne shackle missing from the aft-deck store. When we told the skipper what had happened all he said was, "The bastard. That was a brand-new bloody shackle." '

Finally Keith could resist it no longer and burst into helpless laughter, pointing at the gesticulating spider behind Gerry. Gerry turned around. For a moment he stared at the beast and then he said, 'Well, I suppose that serves me bloody right for not telling you two.'

He pointed at the wall behind us where, lustrous rufous brown against the white plaster, two equally large and equally hairy spiders were going through the same performance.

Personally, I don't really feel strongly about spiders. Certainly, I wouldn't have reacted as violently as at least three of the team who, in their efforts either to kill the beasts or at least put them to flight, knocked furniture over and splattered beer all over the polished floor. In the chaos the generator, always cranky, cut out, and we were left with lamplight alone, so that, in the long deep shadows, every single one of our hairy visitors made a successful escape.

Much later we found out what it was all about. Somewhere in the room had been a female spider, said to be much, much larger than her eight-inch consorts. Unknown to us, she had been sitting there peacefully pumping into the air a scent that every male for a mile around was finding irresistible, despite the fact that for the male to mate successfully he needs to get near this much larger and very venomous creature with the temper of the Red Queen and the predictability of Jack the Ripper. Not surprisingly, he waves a little first from a safe distance, to placate his ever-hungry mate before he makes his final approach. As one of the divers said when I explained all this to him later, 'I never thought I'd say this, but if we were like that I might even go off sex altogether.'

15

They had renamed the dive ship the *Lucky Dragon* when her new owners had taken her over but many of the British crew recognised her from her previous incarnations in the North Sea. Not that she was a bad ship. Certainly she was no longer new but her dive system was one of the seventies-built Strongwork units and it had the solidity of a well tried and tested piece of machinery. During her time in Miri she had been refitted and, with her fresh coat of bright orange paint and her white superstructure, she looked trim and well cared for and ready for sea.

The first job was in the nature of a shakedown operation mainly included on the schedule to allow us to check out our new charge under operating conditions. At a point in the South China Sea marked only by a cross on a chart and a complex of electronic chitters in the computer banks is valve Tango Golf. The job was to inspect the valve, change a main control bundle out and to check the level of oil in the gear boxes. This is the sort of job that is the diving equivalent of weeding, easy to handle, not very interesting but necessary.

To start with the *Lucky Dragon* performed faultlessly. Her positioning system, always a weak point with newly refitted ships, held the ship rock-steady in the open sea without a trace of drift. The dive gases flowed with no hint of leaks, the panel was a model of clean, well maintained efficiency, but of course there was one minor fly in this otherwise perfect ointment.

Lucky Dragon, like many of her kind, uses electric motors to drive the propellers. Direct drive from a diesel motor is too rough, too abrupt in its action for precise moves that might require a ship to shift, say exactly one metre to the left.

The giant Pielstick diesels below decks drive generators to provide that power, and secondarily to provide DC current for the ship's electrics. Such a system relies very heavily on those diesels and their generators, and of course there are back-ups and safety systems in multiple layers to protect us from a total loss of power. The idea of these is to make any possible failure a progressive event, not a catastrophic one, so that the ship might lose urgency in her motion but will never be left dead in the water.

There is one last layer of protection. If all else fails and the drain on the generators, left unchecked, would destroy the system itself, cutout relays open and cut all power from the main engines to the rest of the ship. It is a system that is hardly ever used, but twice during the sea trials of the *Lucky Dragon* the emergency shutdown cut in. We were left a dead ship with no lights and no power other than the low-voltage batteries to the dive-system radios and lighting, and the air motors, crude winches powered by compressed air cylinders, that allow us to recover the bell even if all else fails.

Power loss under trial was an embarrassment to the engineers and a source of self satisfaction to the diving department whose gear was working perfectly. In a few days the fault seemed to go away however and by the time we reached the errant valve with our divers already under pressure and the bell ready to go, we were happy to forgive the ship her teething problems and get on with the job.

It was the kind of night that you only see in the tropics, a sky so deep blue that it was near black but not quite, prickled with the bright points of a southern starfield. We were well into the job, the bell was down and the diver was out, going through the first preliminary checks on the valve gear on the bottom. I was out on deck enjoying the night after a day spent checking lists of drugs that would not balance no matter what. Just as I was about to go below for a drink the power failed again.

It was the same catastrophic failure as before, the lights doused all over the ship so that only the pale glow of the emergency beacons still shone. On the bridge the blood red of the night lamps was replaced by a confused pattern of shadows against the inch thick screens and it was completely silent. The low throb that is always there in a live ship was gone. We were dead in the water, unable to move, unable to do much more than recover the bell on the emergency air-powered lift and wait for developments.

Power failure as such is not a real emergency but all the same I went below to check out the position in saturation control. It was all in hand. The bell was back on the system, the divers safely recovered and everything secured. I was about to leave when the phone rang.

'Jon, that you?' Gerry's voice.

'Yes.'

'Good job you're still on shift. We've got a situation up here. You might need to evacuate.'

'Because of the power?'

'Not exactly. Ten minutes ago Radar picked up a large vessel heading towards us. It's probably a crude carrier. We've tried to raise him on radio of course, but you know what those bastards are like for radio watches or watches of any kind for that matter.'

'How close will he get?'

'Too bloody close by half. Of course we might get lucky, but if he doesn't hit us on his present course we'll be very lucky indeed.'

We had all heard stories of the ULCCs (Ultra-Large Crude Carriers), massive tankers that roam the world's oceans lugging cargoes of oil that run into millions of tonnes. They often never see port, indeed are unable to put into most of the world's harbours, and discharge and load far out to sea at the end of long jetties built especially for the purpose. Because they crew only a few men these monsters run with minimal watches, in theory two men on the bridge and two in the engine room. In practice they are well reputed to run without watches at all, relying on the electronic fingers of radar to warn them of oncoming shipping, and the unseeing automatic hands of the autopilot to guide them across the empty acres of the deep. They are involved in far and away more run-downs than any other kind of ship.

Lucky Dragon was no fishing boat but in a collision with a crude carrier we would simply be swept under, and her crew might not even realise until later that they had hit something.

'We can't raise them at all?' I asked, more to fill in the vacuum than because I expected that we could,

'No. And if they don't respond to radio then they probably don't have a bridge watch. In any case it would take them four miles to stop and they are already too close. We need them to alter course in the next ten minutes or we've got a problem.'

'OK, Gerry,' I said, 'I'll get them ready for hyperbaric escape.'

'No launch till I tell you, OK?'

Below in the control room I briefed my opposite number from the off-duty shift, a young recruit called Darren, and we got to work. Because divers are held under pressure they can't simply be thrown into a lifeboat like lesser mortals. Instead we have a lifeboat containing a pressure chamber, connected to the main living system by a three-foot diameter duct, like a giant adventure playground. The divers climb through to the lifeboat, seal the door, and the gas in the duct is vented to the air, allowing the boat to fall free and isolating it from the ship's dive system. It's a dangerous, last-ditch kind of operation involving perfect drilled responses and good luck to succeed. I picked up the communications set.

'Hello, inside.'

'Hello, Jon. Can't you sleep or what?'

''Fraid not, lads. Look, wake everyone could you, mate? We've got a problem.'

I explained the situation as succinctly as I could, concluding, 'Just in case, I want a hyperbaric evacuation, I'm declaring condition Amber as from now, and I want you in the boat and ready to go.'

They didn't grumble, they didn't bitch, in fact no one said anything much, but they climbed through the hatch towards the lifeboat and vanished off my TV monitor screen. The last man closed the hatch behind him. I called Darren who was two decks above me in the hyperbaric lifeboat, checking the divers' safe arrival at the other end of the ten-metre length of pressure ducting.

'Darren. You reading?'

'Loud and clear.' Thank God for battery back-ups.

'Right, they are on their way. Tell me as soon as you have a seal on the door.'

'OK.'

I waited while he went through the next stage, pumping a little gas into the lifeboat's chamber to seal the door that led back into the ducting, so isolating the little rescue capsule from the ship.

I switched the comms over to the bridge line.

'Bridge, I have ten divers secure in the lifeboat. Request OK to go to launch ready position.'

'Roger that, sat control.'

I opened the valve that would vent the gas out of the duct and squirt three thousand pounds' worth of helium mix into the night air. There was a screech of escaping gas that died through a moan, then a low foghorning note and finally a whisper. I checked the panel and then keyed the mike again.

'Bridge, I have zero pressure on the duct. Ready to launch.'

'Roger, sat control. Hold position Amber until I give the order.'

I left the control room, a pretty final step in a dive ship, for that is the nerve centre, manned day and night. But now I was abandoning it as there was nothing more for me to do there.

The deck was full of crewmen in life jackets, lined up ready beside the four enclosed lifeboats. As each man was checked he took his place, and as each boat was filled it was swung out into the ready position, ready for the order that would come over the deck radios and consign those plastic cockleshells to survive the seas alone.

Inside the hyperbaric boat it was cramped and it smelled of diesel. Most of the space is taken up by the capsule and the onboard reserves of gas. There is only room for one man to sit at the chamber control panel and another, perched above his head in a conning tower, to drive the boat. I strapped myself into the driving seat and checked the gauges. As soon as I turned it on the radio began to squawk.

'All ships, all ships. This is Dive Ship *Lucky Dragon*, we are dead in the water and on collision course with an Ultra-Large Carrier. If you can hear me on the carrier please acknowledge my transmission.'

There was a pause of unbroken static then he started again, 'All ships, all ships . . .'

It was our own radio operator true to the traditions of the service, repeating the electronic warning again and again, trying to avoid a disaster, even if it meant he was the last man left aboard.

From my position at the control console I could see the unbroken darkness where the carrier must be. I knew that there was nothing to do now but wait, but I still couldn't keep my eyes off that patch of dark. Finally I caught her lights, a pattern of glow against the water. She seemed to be headed right for us.

The oncoming ship gradually changed from a few lights, to a pattern of lights, and from a pattern of lights to a bulking shadow against the sea, and then, finally, we could see her plainly, a mountain of a ship, travelling at half ballast, with a bow wave fifty feet across, and a superstructure that reached to the night sky, blotting out that bright tropical starfield.

The radio crackled. 'Right, you bastards,' it said. 'All the bloody luck in the world. First one back to Singapore buys the drinks.'

Then, more formally, 'Control to all stations. All stations Abandon, Abandon, Abandon.'

Beside my right hand was a lever cased in plastic and painted red.
I pulled it hard up. There was a terrific crack as the explosive bolts
let go, a giddy moment of falling, and then a bone jarring impact as
the little boat hit the water. The diesel started with a great rattling
roar and we were free and steering away from the ship and into
the dark.

The tanker was in clear sight by now, still oblivious of the chaos
she had caused, still unaware of approaching catastrophe. The voice
on the main radio had stopped calling, but the deck radio was still
squawking.

'Boat three, clear away.'

'Two, clear away.'

'Four and one, clear away.'

That was all the crew off in any case. I added my own voice to
the chorus, 'Hyperbaric clear away.'

The tanker was like a cathedral ploughing through the night water.
In front of her, the wash of the bow wave crested pale blue with
luminescence, and, at the stern, there was a great plume of foam
where the screw turned. We could hear the engines rumble, even
over our own diesel, and as she passed us we could hear the throb
of that big prop, chewing up the water.

She closed on the *Lucky Dragon*, obscured her from sight for a
moment, and missed her by a mere six feet before ploughing on
through the night to God only knows where.

The radio burst into a shower of expletives. Darren, who was
unable to see out from his position by the panel, was saying, 'What
happened? What the hell happened?' over and over.

'She missed us,' I said, 'she bloody missed us. We can go
home, mate.'

But of course it was easier said than done. Normal lifeboats can
be used in port for running errands from ship to shore. They are
by their nature capable of rejoining the ship. Hyperbaric boats
are intended to leave once and once only, and getting them back,
with their divers inside, is not easy. It took twenty back-breaking,
finger-crushing, temper-fraying hours before we finally had the thing
safe back again on the ship, and the divers were free to re-enter the
comparative luxury of the system.

The day afterwards, Gerry showed me a telegram from the

owners. It was couched in that peculiar English that is used for day-to-day communications in the Far East.

> Understand that Ship conducted UNAUTHORISED emergency drill on high seas yesterday. Please to desist from such practice in future. Most wasteful on gas.
> Signed,
> South China Sea Oceanic Salvage and Towing Company

'What the bloody hell shall I do with this?' he asked.

'Gerry, my old mate,' I said, 'there's no decent answer to that.'

* * *

After the incident with the tanker, the agent, who had until then been interested in us only as a slight diversion to his routine throughput of more conventional ships, became more attentive.

Costings that had gone through without question were suddenly queried at every turn. Each small item of equipment, instead of being shipped out to us by return flight, was delayed or simply not forthcoming.

Gas, Heliox mix, arrives at the ship in racks of sixty-four cylinders called quads. On most ships a major, though tedious, part of the workload of the Life Support department is moving the gas from the quads on deck down, via a heavy reinforced hose, to the hard piping that will carry gas to the compressors in the depths of the ship. To do this job one needs a couple of small, screw-threaded brass fittings to connect the hoses to the cylinders at one end and to the deck lines at the other. When the first shipment of gas to arrive after our game of blindman's bluff with the tanker came, there were no fittings to be found on board.

Gerry was disgusted.

'You're seriously telling me that we can't work for the sake of a ten-quid gas fitting?'

''Fraid so,' I said.

'We have to get around it,' he replied with the air of a man preparing to slice through the Gordian knot.

'How?'

'We'll get the engineers to make us one up.'

'Those fittings are tested to 200 bar, for God's sake.'

'It should be OK if he uses a solid bit of brass.'

Two hours later the fitting was ready. It looked crude because it had two screw threads lathed out of a lump of brass that weighed

maybe four pounds or more. One screw thread fitted into the deck
line, the other into the threaded end of the hose. The trouble was
that it would be expected, at the beginning when the quad was full,
to carry a pressure of 2,800 pounds to the square inch. I wasn't
happy.

'We have to test it first, Gerry,' I said.

'Bollocks. It'll hold.'

'But he just cut it out of a bit of scrap brass, there could be all
kinds of cracks in it,' I said.

I'm not usually the nervous type, but then I would be the one
next to the thing while it was under pressure.

'If you are too scared to turn it on I'll do it,' Gerry said, obviously
expecting this gesture of bravery in the face of danger to call out the
machismo in me. The trouble was that I've seen that trick too often
before.

'OK,' I said, 'you do it then.'

Having made the gesture he had no choice but to carry it through,
so he approached the first fitting with the nonchalance of a man who
walks into the dock to be tried for murder. He cracked the first valve
open just a little. There was a gentle hiss and the polypropylene tube
that had been lying relaxed like a sunning snake on the deck twitched
itself and went rigid. Nothing else happened. Gerry walked back to
where I was standing beside a bulkhead.

'You see?' he said, with the air of a man who has been proved
right in the event. 'I knew it would take it.'

There was a crack like a heavy rifle and a scream of escaping
gas. The hose end whipped across the deck in a murderous arc and
jammed itself into a crevice in a winch housing. Gerry's expression
suddenly became pained.

I sneaked up on the quad from behind, as long as the gas was
escaping there was always the chance that the hose would whip
back again, and reached around to close the valve. The scream of
gas diminished and stopped. I walked back to Gerry.

'Never mind,' I said, proved right in turn, and prepared to be
magnanimous. 'It was a good idea.'

He was pale and clammy and his face was a sick grey colour that
is the clearest warning of all of shock.

'Gerry?' I said.

He turned to show me his back, a second before his legs wobbled
and he half fell, half knelt on to the deck. His right leg was soaked

in fresh blood and there was an ugly hole showing through the rip in his overalls where the piece of flying brass had sliced into him.

In countless Westerns the fall guy, who is shot in the buttock with a .44, is one of the great humorous butts, but in reality it's not quite the same. When a heavy, fairly slow-moving missile strikes flesh and bone it tears a rough cavity below the skin surface and lodges there, together with bits of cloth, dead skin and any other material that it happens to pick up on the way in. The lump of brass that had struck Gerry fitted this scenario nicely. Even so it isn't, and never has been, a simple matter of digging the offending missile out, while the patient shows his true grit by grinding his teeth against the pain, until you finally slap a Band Aid over the spot and drop the slug into a white enamel kidney basin with a satisfying metallic clonk. The trouble was convincing Gerry of that.

He gathered as much authority as he could in the circumstances, which was not a whole lot with his backside exposed to the world and lifted with a pillow under his hips.

'There's no need to fuss over it for God's sake,' he said. 'Dress the bloody thing and I'll be OK after a few days.'

I looked into the depths of the wound. As far as I could see, the metal had remained in one single lump and it was buried in the muscle of the right buttock, well clear of tricky structures like the sciatic nerve and the femoral artery. The trouble was that without X-rays it's hard to be sure.

I gripped a section of the lump and pulled experimentally. It shifted a little and Gerry, craning his neck to see, gave me a dirty look over his right shoulder.

'Are you going to pull the bloody thing out or spend the next hour admiring my bum?' he said.

'Glad to see that you've lost none of your charm, mate.'

The piece of brass that I had hold of seemed loose, so I pulled gently, and it popped clear of the damaged tissue, leaving an ugly red cavity behind it.

'The thing is, Gerry,' I said, swabbing the area with sterile gauze, 'that we should really remove all the tissue that it damaged on the way in.'

'And how exactly are you going to do that?'

'You don't want to know,' I said.

'You are going to cut a lump out of my arse?'

'Nothing so crude.'

He swung his legs off the table and sat up in a lopsided sort of fashion.

'No way.'

'Gerry, if I don't clean it properly you could get all kinds of infection. Also when the anaesthetic wears off you won't half regret leaping about like that.'

'No way are you cutting my arse.'

'All right. So lie back down and I'll dress it instead but it'll have to be an open dressing. I can't suture it in case I bury infection.'

I packed the wound with sterile gauze and antibiotic powder. It would leave a hell of a scar but I didn't suppose that he cared that much.

The problem with such a system of wound management is that it needs the dressing changing day after day, until the cavity is small enough to cover and leave to heal. The crew, forever inquisitive, got to know exactly what was involved and could not resist the chance of deflating Gerry's authority.

He was, by and large, a fair and easy man to work for but he did have one regrettable weakness. At home or in the dockside bars of a dozen ports around the world, he would gather a small, admiring and mainly female audience, and regale them with diving stories that perhaps exaggerated the truth a little. Since his break-up with Sue, his tall stories, and the girls he impressed with them, had got a little out of hand.

On the third day I had Gerry lying once more on the couch, bottom stuck up in the air, and lit by the overhead lights while I prepared the fresh dressings. Despite my misgivings the wound was healing well. Just then the door opened. There was a blur of movement, a click, and then it closed again. The whole thing was so fast that I hardly had time to register it and I assumed that someone had come looking for a bit of medical help, realised that I had a patient and left.

Divers' bars usually have a notice board or a mirror that is studded with the colourful stickers and calling cards of various specialists that have passed that way. Much, much later I found that every divers' bar in South-East Asia was displaying a large full colour photograph of Gerry, trousers around his ankles, hairy buttocks in the air, looking back towards the opening door with an expression of mild surprise on his completely recognisable face.

The injury was barely healed by crew change time. I applied the final elastic dressing to a bright pink scar four days before we were due to steam to the beach for the start of our Christmas leave.

The few days before a crew change are always marked by an odd emotional mix of euphoria and tension. Old-time sailors with memories of their long brutal trips at sea refer to the sleeplessness, excitement and inability to concentrate as 'The Channels', as it was a state of mind familiar to them when the ship sailed past the Wolf Rock and entered the English Channel homeward bound. Today the trips are shorter but the tension is just as great. On the night before we were due to leave station to head for the beach, Gerry called me into his cabin. He was a little subdued.

'I hate to tell you this, Jon,' he said, 'but I think the ship is headed for a lay-up after the next job.'

If this was true it would mean the effective end of the contract for us, as our relief crew would complete the scheduled work. Still, it is almost a matter of etiquette to pretend indifference under such circumstances.

'Well, we've been there before, mate,' I said. 'It isn't the end of the world.'

'No, but it could be a long time before she works again.'

'You mean I should look for another ship after Christmas?'

'Jon, I wish we were coming back here, but, yes I think so.'

'Well, thanks for letting me know. What will you do?'

'Me? Oh, there's a lady in Dubai who wants to mother me.'

'God help her,' I said. 'Oh yes, and go easy with that wound. I don't want her suing me if it opens up in a moment of passion.'

He thought for a moment, then said, 'Look, are you going back to the UK?'

'Of course.'

'I'll give you the number of a bloke I know who might just be able to help you find another ship. I did hear he was getting into the salvage game.'

'Salvage? Sounds good.'

He shook his head and laughed. 'Some day,' he said, 'Judy will have me killed for getting you into this job you know?'

'I don't think so, Gerry. Sue might have you killed though.'

'Well, you know what Billy Young said about dive crews?'

'No.'

'He said that you have to love the guys, but you wouldn't want your daughter to marry one.'

He laughed then said, 'Well, the man's name is Steve, Steve Harrison. Give him a ring.'

Christmas came and went. I enjoyed my leave, revelled in the warmth and good company, and finally, when the holly was finally wilting and the turkeys long reduced to bones, I phoned the number that Gerry had given me.

Three days afterwards I was at a twelfth night party at home. It was very late indeed and the weather, as it often is in the early days of the New Year in our corner of the North, was foul. Outside the snow was flurrying in white saucers out of a three o'clock in the morning sky the colour of lead.

Steve Harrison, a tough-looking forty-year-old veteran of a hundred dive projects and more, was sitting drinking a glass of mulled red wine misted by the spices to the colour of a dusty ruby. Our wives, friends already after a six-hour acquaintance, were swapping notes.

'I think,' Steve said at length, 'that I might have a job for you this year.'

Jenny, Steve's wife, looked at him in exasperation.

'For heaven's sake,' she said, 'have you only just got around to telling him? You decided that hours ago.'

Steve was not in the least fazed.

'Actually,' he said, 'it's an interesting project. What it is, is . . .'

But that, as they say, is quite another story.

Glossary

2Ws	Wharton and Williams. A company founded by Rick Wharton and Malcolm Williams. It also had a Norwegian arm, Wharton Williams and Wilhelmson, 3Ws. Both companies are now trading under the Rockwater International banner.
AGE	Arterial Gas Embolus. Gas in a main artery. The most dangerous of all decompression accidents.
Ampicillin	Trade mark for a branded penicillin-based drug.
Anaphylaxis	An acute, often potentially fatal, reaction to a foreign protein.
batter	The splay on underwater steel work that makes the base of a platform much wider than its top.
bell umbilical	A heavy line carrying services from the mother ship to the diving bell.
blow-out	An uncontrolled escape of gas and oil from a well.
bomber	The technician in charge of X-ray work.
bombing	X-ray inspecting a weld for defects.
BOP	Blow-Out Preventer. A complex of valves fitted to an oil well to prevent sudden uncontrolled escapes of oil and gas.
BP	Blood pressure reading.
Broco torch	An underwater cutting torch that uses oxygen and a hollow metal rod stuffed with iron wire to burn through steel.
camp boss	Person in charge of catering services.
cannula	A plastic tube introduced into a surface vein

through the skin and used to administer intra-venous fluids.

comealong — A hand power ratchet winch system for shifting small loads

comms — Industry shorthand for Communication System, either ship to ship, or surface crew to diver, or crew to crew.

Cordtex — A plastic-covered detonating fuse used to initiate high explosives under water.

CPR — Cardio-Pulmonary Resuscitation. Mouth to mouth with heart massage.

D5W — One of a number of plasma expanders administered to replace lost circulation volume when in shock or simply to keep an IV line open if needed. Basically just salt water.

débridement — Removal of dead tissue from a wound, to reduce the risk of infection and speed healing.

DP — Dynamic Positioning. A system of propellers that allows a ship to hold position in open water.

drive off — Loss of control of the positioning system causing the ship to move suddenly off station.

DSV — Dive Support Vessel. A specialised ship thats only real function is to provide diving services.

ECG — Electro Cardio Graph. A measure of the electrical activity in the heart either displayed on a screen or relayed by radio to specialist help on the beach.

Ethilon — The most common suture material for closing wounds in the skin.

Flamazine — Trade name for silver sulphadiazine cream used for the treatment of burns.

gassified water incident — Situation where there are so many gas bubbles from an out of control well that the water no longer supports ships, that then sink like stones.

halon — A mixture of tetra chloro and tetra fluoro methanes. Halon is a gas stored in cylinders and piped to high-risk fire areas. If there is a fire the halon floods the area and snuffs out the flame.

Heliox	Helium and oxygen mixture used for breathing in deep dives.
hit	Slang term for decompression sickness.
hot water suit	A diving suit with tubes that carry hot sea water from the surface to keep a diver warm.
hyperbaric lifeboat	A lifeboat modified to hold a diving pressure chamber inside. This can be used to evacuate divers in event of an emergency.
IV	Intravenous, referring to injected drugs administered directly into a vein.
jacket	The steel tower that a platform rests on. A large one can be several hundred feet high.
KMB 17	A modern plastic shelled diving helmet. The industry standard equipment.
Largactil	Chlorpromazine. A strong sedative.
lignocaine	A local anaesthetic used for stitching skin wounds, dental work etc.
LST	Life Support Technician. A person in charge of running all aspects of the pressurised living quarters.
medecut	A type of cannula.
medevac	Term originated in Vietnam, meaning a helicopter evacuation of an injured man to a hospital. (Americans call this a 'dust off'.)
midnight salvage	An illegal salvage operation carried out without the insurers' permission.
neoprene	Soft conforming rubber material used in close-fitting divers' undersuits.
niggles	Low-grade pains associated with decompression.
Omnopon	A morphine-based pain killer.
panel	The control panel for the diving system.
pneumo cuff	An inflatable rubber cuff used mostly for blood pressure measurements.
pneumothorax	Air escaping from a ruptured lung gathering in the chest cavity.
Rat Hat	Ratcliff Helmet. A type of diving helmet.
riser	The steel pipe carrying oil and gas from the underwater wells to the platform.
ROV	Remote controlled vehicle. A swimming TV

	camera with manipulator arms that can survey under water and carry out some subsea operations.
RTA	Medical term for a road traffic accident.
sarin and tabun	The earliest developed of the organophosphate nerve gases. Developed but never saw use in the 1914–18 war. Dumped in huge volumes after the Second World War.
superquad or quad	A steel rack of sixty-four fifty-litre gas bottles.
synflex	Incredibly tough plastic, reinforced pressure hose used to pipe gases.
tetracycline	An antibiotic-type drug used to control infection.
tugger	A small air-powered winch.
ULCC	Ultra-Large Crude Carrier. A very large tanker used to ferry oil around the world by sea.
umbilical	A complex of tubes and wires tethering the diver and carrying gases, hot water and communications links.
Venflon	A type of IV cannula.